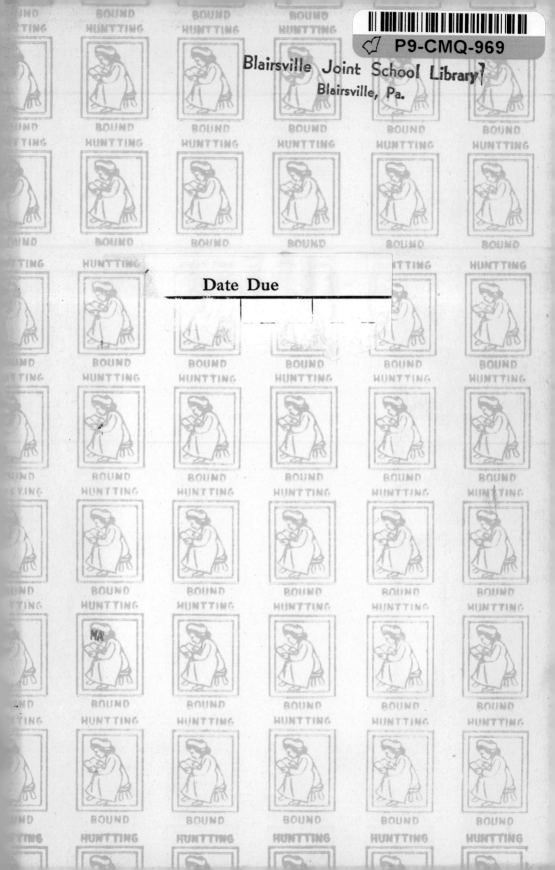

BRIDGES

THE VIKING PRESS

New York · 1956

BRIDGES

Written and illustrated by

HENRY BILLINGS

CONTENTS

ACKNOWLEDGMENTS

For help and advice in the preparation of *Bridges,* the author wishes to thank the following:

The American Cable Company; Mr. O. H. Ammann, consulting engineer; The Department of City Planning, City and County of San Francisco; Mr. Shortridge Hardesty, consulting engineer; Prof. James K. Finch, Renwick Professor Emeritus in Civil Engineering, Columbia University; Mr. W. E. Jessup, Editor, Civil Engineering Magazine; Mr. T. T. McCrosky, city and regional planning consultant; New York State Bridge Authority; The Port of New York Authority; Mr. R. E. Royall, Bureau of Public Roads, Washington, D. C.; Dr. David B. Steinman, consulting engineer; Mr. Julian Street, United States Steel Corporation.

The author also wishes to make special mention of the invaluable aid given him in the preparation of Chapter X by Mr. James N. O'Gorman, Instructor in Civil Engineering, Columbia University.

BRIDGES

I. Where the Road Meets the River

MOST of the bridges in the United States have been built to carry wagon roads, railroads, or today's superhighways across natural or man-made obstacles. A bridge is part of a road, and without roads and bridges our complex system of land transportation could not exist. But bridges are more than just useful structures. They are the familiar and romantic landmarks of our countryside. They also serve as the gateways to our cities, and their majestic grace and beauty set them apart from the crowded streets and jumbled buildings.

As one looks across a mountain landscape, it is difficult to remind oneself that the grandeur of those soaring, rocky peaks merely represents the heaving and buckling of the earth's crust.

9

Generally we are prompted to whisper the word "eternal" as our eyes try to take in the geological chaos caused by the relatively sudden loss of surface heat a million-odd years ago. For a moment let us imagine that this cooling-off process occurred more slowly, and the inevitable shrinking was so slight that the land areas of the planet remained flat, uniform layers of smooth rock. Under such circumstances we might never have had to build a road; we could now motor about our continent in any direction our fancy chose, or, as in a modern airplane, we could drive directly on a specified "great circle" to our destination. Fortunately this did not happen. The beauty of mountains, valleys, hills, and rivers is well worth the labor of building roads and bridges.

A road is the means by which we avoid or pass over the thousand and one difficulties that make the countryside through which we move an ever-changing and fascinating panorama. From a distance a mountain range may appear insurmountable, but as long as any sort of road is indicated on the filling-station map we go on climbing, confident that we will get through regardless of the steep hairpin curves. However, there are other natural obstacles which, though not as dramatic as a mountain range, will even more surely bring the traveler to a standstill. Streams, rivers, estuaries, and arms of the sea, as well as tidal marshes, swamps, gorges, and escarpments—any of these can bring the highway to an end. Here, where the road meets the river, civilized man's ingenuity usually asserts itself and constructs a bridge in one form or another, so that the road may continue to its destination.

When the first fixed roadways began to link village to village and town to town, the building and rebuilding of bridges inevitably followed. Except for temporary military bridges like those of Julius Caesar or our own Bailey Bridges of the last war, the first consideration was to make them as permanent as possible. This meant that the bridge designer had to match his skill

and experience against the special hazards of the particular obstacle that had to be overcome. Besides the destructive forces
of flood, tide, wind, and fire, he soon learned that he had to take
into account the kind and amount of traffic that would use his
bridge. A footbridge might have served a community for generations, but when the path leading to it became a road filled
with carts and wagons, then the original bridge, no matter how
sound it might be, would have to be replaced.

A man on foot, carrying a thirty-pound load, can improvise
many ways to cross a river. Stepping stones, fallen logs, shallow
sand bars, or hanging vines—one means or another will usually
get him to the other side without too great risk of dunking his
valuables. In many countries the dangers of swift-running
streams were surmounted by primitive forms of suspension
bridges. The Peruvians wove fiber cables strong enough to span a
hundred-and-fifty-foot river when strung from giant trees along
the bank. There is a prehistoric form of hanging bridge, which
looks like an elongated hammock, that is still used in northern
India to cross the narrow mountain gorges of the Himalayas. In

ancient times, the Chinese evolved a method by which a man could be hauled across a stream while sitting in a kind of sling that dangled from a stout cable, much like our own breeches buoy. The early lake dwellers of Europe built crude wooden footbridges to help them over swamps and mires. In Ireland, nimble travelers leaped the salmon streams by means of specially placed stepping stones.

It was the horse-drawn vehicle, whether sled, cart, or wagon, that called for wider and stronger bridges. Stone and wood were the only materials used for bridgebuilding up to the end of the eighteenth century. In the form of stone arches or wooden trusses they bore the weight of the horse-drawn traffic that moved along the roads of Europe. With the coming of the Industrial Revolution, iron and later steel were used in the construction of bridges. These new materials could barely keep pace with the increasing speed and weight of the steam locomotive. Modern high-tension steel now makes it possible for us to carry our superhighways over wider natural barriers than ever before. Fortunately the steel suspension bridge passed out of the experimental stage long before we were burdened with sixty million motorcars.

The shape or form of a bridge is determined in large part by the materials with which it is built. With the introduction of each new bridgebuilding material, whether stone, wood, iron, or steel, new shapes arose. In Chapter X there is an attempt to explain graphically how bridges do their work—or more simply, how they support themselves and their loads through the correct use of the materials that go into their construction.

When Alice was in Wonderland she was able to grow bigger or smaller merely by eating a bite of the Caterpillar's mushroom. However, there seems to be no magic formula for reducing the number of motorcars that clog our cities and throng the "thruways." Neither two world wars nor the depression of the 1930s did more than temporarily flatten the rising curve of motor-vehicle registrations. During the last forty years no one dreamed that the rate of increase would continue unchecked. In 1915, when there were three and a half million cars on the road, everyone hailed the new motor age and agreed that the motorcar had finally replaced the horse. Since then almost all serious estimates—even the highest—about the future increase in the volume of traffic have been consistently wrong. As the speed of the low-priced car rose, our traffic planning fell farther and farther behind. Until recently we have always underestimated the human factor in this situation. At the very start we failed to recognize the popularity of motoring as a sport; later, when organized touring became a national recreation, we never guessed that so many people wanted to see America first—on wheels. During the depression the last thing a man would give up was the family car and the first thing he bought when he got a job was a new car. Today there are few communities in the United States that are not totally dependent on motor transportation.

This is a book on bridges in this country, not on the traffic problem as such. However, it is the constant and unrelenting pressure caused by the growth in vehicular traffic that has brought about one of the most astounding periods of bridge-building the world has ever seen. Within the last thirty years more than a hundred great vehicular bridges have been constructed, almost all of them designed to meet the needs of the light, fast, modern automobile. Whereas our early stone bridges and timber bridges were made possible through the special knowledge and skills brought to us from Europe, the development of the long-span suspension bridge is strictly an American achievement. Seventy-five years ago the Brooklyn Bridge's quarter-mile leap across the East River filled the world with wonder. Today the main span of the Golden Gate Bridge soars for three-quarters of a mile above the open waters of the Pacific. Tomorrow the Narrows Bridge may stretch its arms a full mile across New York harbor.

These of course are spectacular bridges that stand as monuments to the genius of our contemporary bridgebuilders. But these bridges also symbolize a much older and deeper characteristic of those who settled this continent—the need for freedom of movement. In satisfying this need we have built one of the most extensive systems of land transportation in the world. It is also unique, in that the older free roads of this country are now being interlaced with an intricate pattern of high-speed "thruways" that give the individual motorist greater freedom of speed and direction, as well as greater comfort, all of which he is willing to pay for as he uses them. Superhighways require superbridges, but these are only a part of the picture, for in order to maintain freedom of movement on our three million miles of roads at least three hundred thousand bridges, large and small, are in constant use.

And so, before taking up the great suspension bridges that link our superhighways, it might be well to consider the common bridges that we use every day and scarcely notice. Whether it is the old wooden bridge over Horse Creek or the wrought-iron truss over the river, when a bridge burns down or washes away, or is merely closed for repairs, we are forcibly reminded that the continuity of the road depends on bridges and that without them a precious heritage—the freedom of movement—is drastically curtailed.

II. A Continent without Bridges

TODAY we can cross the continent in eight hours by plane without being concerned about the question of bridges. The early explorers, however, did their traveling at water level. They chose to use the rivers and estuaries as natural pathways into the interior. It is interesting to note that in the course of thousands of miles on the great mid-continental river systems these newcomers never reported seeing a single bridge built by Indians. Captain John Smith does mention a kind of primitive causeway made of saplings and forked sticks that crossed one of the tidal marshes near Jamestown. His soldiers, fearing that this was a bear trap, preferred to flounder through the mud to dry land. The North American Indian, when confronted by a wide, deep river, moved along the bank until he could find some friendly river tribe to paddle him over, or, if he feared that his ferryman would take him prisoner, put together a temporary raft of floating logs and wild grapevines barely seaworthy enough for one crossing.

It was from just such a raft that George Washington fell into the icy waters of the Allegheny River. He was returning to Virginia in the winter of 1753, after delivering Governor Robert Dinwiddie's note to the French officer at Fort LeBoeuf, in an attempt to avert the French and Indian Wars. According to young Major Washington's account of the journey, both crossings of the river had been rugged. On the way out to the fort he and his guide had to swim their horses across, though the river was at flood stage, and on the way back his companion nearly died of exposure and frostbite. Even at that time there were already a few well-known Indian trails that crossed the Alleghenies, but all of them—like Nemacolin's Trail, which Washington followed—ended on the banks of the Ohio or one of its tributaries.

Three years later, on Major Washington's advice, General Edward Braddock led his British regulars over the same pathway. Starting from Cumberland, in the western part of Maryland, Braddock was determined to build a true wagon road through the wilderness. After months of slow, dogged labor, a rough wood road only wide enough for one wagon was hacked out of the forest. The road ended at a clearing on the edge of the Monongahela River, and so did the military expedition, for it was here that Braddock's army was ambushed by the French and Indians. For years this trail was known as Braddock's Road, but there is no record that any attempt was ever made permanently to bridge the small rivers winding through the upland country of Maryland and Pennsylvania.

The Indian word "Ohio" (*oyo*) means "beautiful," and the fertile river valley of that name became the goal of overland expeditions just after the Revolution. Whether one followed the old Nemacolin's Trail or took Boone's Wilderness Road or went by way of the Lancaster Turnpike to Pittsburgh, to get there meant fording streams, clambering across narrow mountain gorges, building corduroy roads over swampy ground, or rafting the wagon and cattle down the larger tributaries. In other words, there were no bridges on these trails leading to the Ohio, and, once the traveler arrived on its banks, none to carry him across its broad muddy waters. Another half-century passed before travel westward could be favorably compared to covering the same distance on the continent of Europe.

The first improvement began in 1806, when Congress passed an act authorizing the construction of a national turnpike from Cumberland, Maryland, west to the Ohio River. Thomas Jefferson appointed the road commissioners and it was decided that the new highway should follow the pathway used by Washington and Braddock. When first planned, this "National Pike" was to run from the Maryland tidewater to the farthest western outpost, St. Louis on the Mississippi. Today U.S. Route 40 follows much the same path across the states and completes what was not finished in the nineteenth century.

In its heyday, before the Civil War, the National Pike was the longest and most important road in the United States. Along the turnpike between Baltimore and Wheeling (then in Virginia) one could find almost every kind of bridge built in America at that period. These had to be stout bridges to carry the huge, swaying Conestoga wagons, laden with five tons of freight and drawn by six heavy dray horses. Some are still in use today, carrying Route 40 and its swiftly moving modern traffic over the same streams and rivers of that picturesque countryside.

However, the history of bridgebuilding in this country did not begin with bridges on the National Pike. Long before that road came into existence, bridges were built across the Connecticut and Schuylkill Rivers. These first permanent bridges, made entirely of wood, were masterpieces of timber construction. They set the pattern for the thousands of covered bridges that were built from Maine to California.

One of the earliest permanent bridges on this continent was built by Enoch Hale in 1785, across the Connecticut River. The site chosen was at Bellows Falls, Vermont, where the river is narrow and a reef of rocks forms an island in midstream. This bridge was made entirely of white pine, with a total length of about 350 feet, each span being somewhat less than 100 feet. Hale was a shrewd Yankee trader; he had placed his toll bridge not only at the best natural crossing, but also on the main route between Boston and Montreal. This was not a covered bridge, but because of the fine quality of workmanship and the soundness of the first-growth timbers used in its construction, it lasted for more than fifty years with only minor repairs. Hale was a business promoter and not a professional bridgebuilder. Despite the fact that the tolls from the Bellows Falls bridge ultimately proved that it was an excellent investment, he never built another bridge.

Although the covered bridges of Vermont are today the most famous and most highly esteemed by antiquarians, it was on the roads leading into Philadelphia in the early 1800s that some of the longest and most ingenious timber bridges were built. However, of the three famous pioneer bridgebuilders in this country—Timothy Palmer, Theodore Burr, and Louis Wernwag—the first two learned the art of timber construction in New England. Palmer's most famous bridge was known as the "Permanent Bridge" and was built in 1806 to carry the final stretch of the Lancaster Pike across the Schuylkill River and into

Philadelphia. This was an exceptionally long bridge for those days, and its three spans were designed in the form of trussed arches. Judging from what information we have, this was not a covered bridge. Later, after building many bridges in New York State and elsewhere, Palmer pointed out that if a wooden bridge was protected from the weather it would last twenty to forty years longer than an unprotected one. The gable roof of a covered bridge does help to shed an accumulation of snow, and—far more important—it protects the timber joints from dry rot. If these carefully fitted joints become soft, or "punky," the structure loses its rigidity, and in time its supporting beams begin to

sag of their own weight. On the other hand, there was no possible protection from fire, which became the great destroyer of wooden bridges. The Permanent Bridge, despite its name, went up in flames after fifty years of service.

There was a great boom in land travel up and down the Atlantic coast after the Revolution. One of the worst bottlenecks in the system of roads between Boston and Charleston, South Carolina, was the ferry across the Delaware at Trenton, New Jersey. Besides the local traffic to and from Philadelphia, the road was filled with farm wagons and heavy drays moving south to reach the Lancaster Pike on their way westward. To add to the congestion the drovers used the thoroughfare to get their cattle to the new market ports of New York and Baltimore. The legislatures of New Jersey and Pennsylvania, after recognizing that the ferry service at Trenton was wholly inadequate, appropriated eighteen thousand dollars for a permanent bridge to be designed by Theodore Burr.

The New Englander's skill as a wood joiner is well known. His barns, his wooden bridges, and his clipper ships are all proof of his ingenuity in putting to good use the magnificent virgin forests that hemmed the coves along the coast and lined the river banks. Theodore Burr came from Connecticut, and though there is no mention of his having been apprenticed to a shipwright or a carpenter, he understood the basic principles of building a strong framed structure that would not sag or change its shape.

A short covered bridge is very much like a barn with its ends left open. By the addition of extra diagonal bracing that would tie the upper and lower beams or chords together, such a barn could serve as a bridge. Most wooden bridges are supported by two parallel timber trusses resting on stone abutments. Burr's special innovation was the placing of a heavy bow or arch the length of these two trusses. The arch was fastened securely to the uprights and diagonals that formed the truss, while the two ends of the arch extended below the floor of the bridge and rested on the masonry foundations. As others have pointed out many times, instead of strengthening the arch by means of a truss, as did Timothy Palmer and others, Burr strengthened the truss by means of the arch.

The virtues of the Burr truss were soon recognized by local bridge carpenters, though of course they made their own slight variations. Burr patented his method of construction, but there is good reason to believe that his rural imitators, whether in Vermont or California, never knew they were infringing on his patent. In one form or another his arch truss was used wherever timber bridges were built for the next hundred years, and what Burr lost in royalties he gained in immortality. One of his earliest bridges across the upper Hudson at Waterford, New York, stood for one hundred and five years in continuous service until it too was destroyed by fire.

One of the longest and most handsome wooden-bridge structures built in the early nineteenth century was Louis Wernwag's
"Colossus" Bridge, which also crossed the Schuylkill, near Philadelphia. This bridge had a clear span of 340 feet and was wide
enough to carry two lanes of traffic. It was supported by five

parallel trussed arches, was completely roofed, and was sided with evenly spaced windows to let in the light. It was a graceful and elegant bridge, with its neoclassic portals; after it burned down in 1835, the citizens of Philadelphia mourned the loss not only of a useful bridge, but also of a beautiful monument.

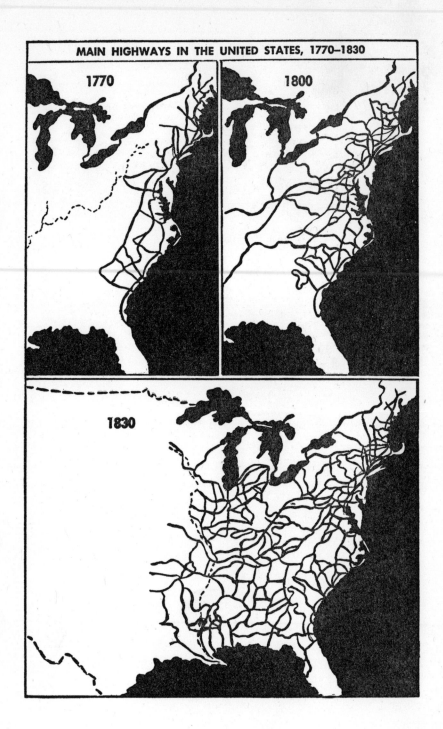

MAIN HIGHWAYS IN THE UNITED STATES, 1770–1830

1770

1800

1830

III. Wagon Bridges (1800-1860)

THE conquest of great distances is one of the oldest and most persistent dreams of this country. This desire sprang quite naturally from our experiences in exploring and settling this continent. The plan for a national pike which would serve as a great highway westward was the first attempt by the federal government to make this dream a reality. As the three maps opposite indicate, what little travel there was beyond the coastal plain was hampered first by the Appalachian range, then by the Ohio, and finally by the Mississippi. The successful bridging of these two rivers had to wait until long after the first flood of settlers had built their towns and cities throughout the length of both river valleys. The National Pike between Baltimore and Wheeling had been in daily use for more than thirty years before Colonel Charles Ellet completed his bridge across the Ohio in 1849. But during those thirty years a variety of bridges had been built over the mountain streams and rivers, thus making the trip by stagecoach from Chesapeake Bay to the Ohio one of the fastest and best-regulated stage lines in the country.

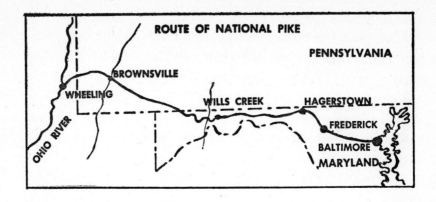

By our standards today the old National Pike was little more than a wide dirt road punctuated with sharp turns and steep grades. It was a simple matter to widen the already existing road to Cumberland, but from there on, the way led through rough Allegheny country; it was not until 1818, twelve years after Congress had appropriated the necessary money, that the pike was opened for through traffic to Wheeling. In fact, by the time the pike was opened to the banks of the Ohio, some of the older original roadway, like that between Frederick and Hagerstown, had fallen into such disrepair that stagecoaches in winter had a hard time getting through. While this section was being repaired a new stone-arch bridge was built across Antietam Creek. The bridge is still standing and is still a sound piece of masonry; its three simple arches of native limestone stride sturdily across the little creek and bear witness to the skill and craftsmanship of the German stonemasons who built it.

There were more than a dozen fine stone bridges on the old pike. All were built more or less in the same style and all used native stone taken from local quarries. Legend has it that the one over Conococheague Creek in Maryland served as a model for all the rest. The adjective "permanent" certainly seems to fit these particular bridges, for the Wills Creek bridge across a rocky gorge known as the Narrows carried its loads for more than a hundred years. During the Civil War there were skirmishes on and around the Antietam bridge, but the light field artillery of that day had little effect on these solid stone structures. One of the earliest stone-arch bridges on the old pike was the Jug Bridge, so named because on its eastern abutment there stands a large stone carved in the shape of a jug; the story goes that a demijohn of whiskey lies beneath it, sealed in with loving care by the head stonemason.

The two decades between 1820 and 1840 were great days for the old National Pike. The stagecoaches kept to their schedules and the inns and taverns were crowded with travelers moving in both directions. Businessmen, real-estate promoters, and politicians from the new state of Ohio hurried eastward to straighten out their affairs in Washington, while the new settlers coming from the abandoned farms of New England, New York, and Pennsylvania pushed slowly westward in their farm wagons. On any section of the pike one might find the traffic heavy and mixed. At the eastern entrance to the covered wooden bridge at Middletown, six or eight Conestoga wagons piled high with freight might have to wait while drovers herded their bellowing, clattering cattle through the bridge's dark interior on their way to the market in Baltimore. Many using the pike trudged along on foot—the wretched gangs of slaves, for instance, chained together, moving slowly toward Wheeling, to be shipped down the river to the new plantations along the Mississippi. And so the planks of the wooden bridges and the dusty surfaces of the stone arches felt the weight of the naked feet, the hobnail shoes, the narrow metal tires of light buggies and rigs, as well as the wide iron rims bearing four tons of freight that moved slowly across their surfaces.

Regardless of the method of travel, the traffic on the old pike had one common quality: it moved slowly. As a result the sharp right-angle curves that led the roadway onto and from certain stone-arch bridges were not really hazardous even to the

swaying stagecoach rattling along at twelve miles an hour. These particular bridges are known as "S" bridges and were built mostly on the western section of the pike just before it reached Wheeling. There was a famous "S" bridge across Middle Wheeling Creek which made a particularly awkward crossing of the stream—and all to satisfy the whim of a charming local lady. The lady, Lydia Sheppard, was determined to have the pike pass her farm and had successfully appealed to Henry Clay, at that time a commissioner of the road. The bridge, with its sharp ninety-degree turns, stood where Mrs. Sheppard wanted it until 1936, when, after many accidents, due simply to the fact that traffic was now moving four times faster than when the bridge was built, the alignment of the road was changed and a new highway bridge erected.

Henry Clay was a constant traveler on the National Pike; once as he was crossing Dunlap's Creek on an old wooden bridge, the weary structure gave way, gently dumping the statesman into the stream below. As he was helped up the bank, he was overheard to remark angrily that here was a case where "mud

and clay did not mix." Whether this incident had any bearing on
the construction of the first iron bridge in this country is not
certain. However, in 1839 a cast-iron bridge was erected over
Dunlap's Creek at Brownsville, Pennsylvania. This bridge was
built with the last federal appropriation for the National Pike,
just before the whole project was given back to the various states
through which the roadway ran. The iron bridge was designed
and erected by Army engineers, who conceived the idea of using
the local foundries to make the castings. The span of the bridge
was 80 feet. It was supported by five parallel arched ribs,
each rib consisting of nine hollow cast-iron sections. The deck
or surface of the bridge was carried on cast-iron supports rising
from these arches. The red lead and aluminum paint used on
metal bridges today was unknown, but a priming coat of tar
and three coats of white lead kept the bridge from rusting.
Though built for horse-drawn vehicles, this first all-metal bridge
lasted well into the twentieth century, carrying heavy trucks
and automobiles going at far higher speeds than its designers
ever dreamed of.

Even before the National Pike had been completed as far west as the Ohio, Wheeling was already one of the busiest river towns between Louisville and Pittsburgh. Within one three-month period more than eight hundred pioneer wagons were ferried across or put on barges to float downstream to other landings. Where the Ohio passes Wheeling there is a thin strip of island that divides the river into a shallow western channel and a broader, deeper eastern one. In 1836 a wooden bridge was built across the western channel, and the up-and-coming citizens of Wheeling were eager to continue the bridge right across to the eastern bank. Only the Supreme Court of the United States was able to stop them by pointing out that such a bridge would block the fleet of steamboats going up and down to Pittsburgh.

Colonel Charles Ellet, a Paris-trained engineer, came up with a bold counter-proposal. He would erect a suspension bridge high enough to permit all but the very tallest smokestacks on the largest steamers to pass underneath; these few boats could do what those on the Seine do—namely, lower their stacks when passing under the bridge. Though this would be a mortifying procedure for the proud skippers of those stately river craft, the government gave its blessing. Ellet immediately began designing what would be the first suspension bridge over one thousand feet in length.

Ellet was already recognized as a daring and original bridge-builder. After the burning of the "Colossus" Bridge on the Schuylkill, he had replaced it with a light suspension bridge supported by wire cables. His next audacious feat was an attempt to span the 800-foot gorge just below Niagara Falls. At the start of this undertaking he offered a prize to the first boy to fly a kite across the river. Once the light string of the kite dangled over the chasm, it was an easy matter to draw heavier and heavier cords, until finally a metal cable was slung across, 200 feet above the foaming surface of the water. Due to a revision of plans, only a light footbridge was built, but Ellet,

always a good showman, was the first to cross it, riding a horse over the narrow, swaying planks.

The two masonry towers of the Wheeling bridge were topped by rollers on which the supporting cables rested, thus allowing for the necessary flexibility. The deck of the bridge, 24 feet in width, was made of oak planking and the distance between the towers was 1010 feet. It is doubtful that Ellet had exact knowledge of the maximum load capacity of his bridge. He merely claimed that it would support the "greatest transitory weight that would ever be." After it was finished, in 1849, the local paper stated that "this bridge will no doubt last long as a monument of American skill and enterprize."

Five years later, to the delight of the people of Pittsburgh, the main span collapsed in what was referred to as a "tornado." There is no record of the actual wind force, but undoubtedly Ellet's bridge was too light and lacked sufficient stiffening or wind bracing. Ellet, as a professional bridgebuilder, was not alone in his miscalculation of wind forces on suspension bridges, and it has taken nearly a century for bridge engineers to understand the complex and unpredictable effects of high winds on suspended structures. The famous bridgebuilder John Roebling first appears on the scene as the man who carried out success-

fully those projects that Ellet had so boldly planned. Where
Ellet got no further than a footbridge over Niagara, Roebling
built a railway bridge, and it was Roebling who rebuilt the
Wheeling bridge two years after it failed. The Wheeling bridge
still stands and still is in use, its heavy cables supporting a
wooden floor that is safe for six-ton loads.

In 1830 the Baltimore and Ohio Railroad's diminutive "Tom
Thumb" locomotive raced a gallant white horse belonging to
one of the stagecoach companies that operated on the National
Pike. As you may know, the little locomotive proved the faster,
but it had engine trouble, and the horse came into the station
first. It was another twenty-three years before the B & O
established its freight and passenger service as far west as
Wheeling. Stagecoaches on the old pike disappeared in the early

1850s. The last hundred miles of this famous highway were never completed to St. Louis, for by the time the roadway was improved as far west as Vandalia, Illinois, the iron horse with its iron bridges came puffing along close behind. Though the bridges on the old pike were maintained for local traffic, the road itself went to pieces from neglect, the taverns and inns closed down, and for more than two generations the pike was used only by neighboring farmers to haul their produce to the nearest railroad station.

As the industrial and farming communities sprang up in the Middle West, the network of roads connecting them spread westward and the building of stone-arch and covered wooden bridges continued as before. For the most part, these highway bridges were constructed on the old rule-of-thumb methods handed down from one generation of carpenters to the next. Hundreds of "S" bridges and covered bridges are still used on the rural highways of Ohio and Indiana. The wooden bridge bears witness that the original forest cover once extended to the Mississippi and, though new kinds of processed bridgebuilding materials like iron and steel were being introduced in the east, the thrifty farmers in these parts preferred to use local materials as long as they were easily available.

The greatest changes in the design and construction of bridges have occurred only within the last hundred and fifty years. Wrought iron and the steam locomotive ushered in a new era of bridgebuilding. The craft of building permanent bridges with natural materials goes back many thousands of years, and it is difficult to appreciate the radical innovations in modern bridge construction and design without some knowledge of the ancient tradition of bridgebuilding. Therefore, before going on with the story of the boom in railroad-bridge building in this country after the Civil War, let us briefly note the development of the stone-arch bridge from the Roman Empire to eighteenth-century France.

IV. Stone Arch and Metal Truss

UNTIL very recently, if one wished to erect a building, a bridge, or a monument that would last, it was natural and traditional to use stone, which is the most enduring of all materials. When a village grew into a town and needed a new bridge, it was the expert stonemason who became the bridgebuilder. But how to make a bridge span out of single stones that could be readily moved was no simple problem. The first permanent stone bridges were made of long, rectangular slabs of stone placed on crude foundations that were little more than piles of rubble. The difficulty was that these early stone bridges could span only very narrow streams.

From these slab or "clapper" bridges to the stone arches was a long and revolutionary step—perhaps comparable only to the introduction of the wooden wheel. Historians agree that no one man could have thought of anything as simple and at the same time astounding as the self-supporting stone arch. There must have been many failures through many generations before it was demonstrated that one could carefully place single stones over an arched wooden form, and, after arranging these stones correctly, could remove the form, leaving each stone so firmly wedged and locked to the next one that all the stones would form a solid, durable structure. It was the Romans who perfected stone bridges and it was their semicircular stone arches that carried the Roman roads across natural barriers, making possible one of the first great systems of land transportation.

However, it took the Romans many centuries to learn to build a bridge like the Pons Augustus, pictured opposite. Their early bridges were little more than masonry dams with stone-arch culverts through which the rivers passed. Inevitably—whether in one year or in ten—the river would rise and wash the bridge away. Only by increasing the size of the arches could the Romans turn the dam into a true bridge that would allow the highest flood waters to pass freely underneath. The five semicircular arches of the Pons Augustus, built by order of the emperor five years before the birth of Christ, were designed to let the river through even at flood stage, and so this imperial monument has continued to serve its community for almost two thousand years. Judging from the fact that the whole surface is faced with marble and that at one time marble porticos marked its entrances, it would seem that this bridge from the start had been planned as an important structure; yet its designer and builder remain unknown. But this is not unusual, for there are only two professional bridgebuilders in the long history of the empire whose names are known to us today: Lucius Fabricus, an engineer of the city of Rome, and Caius Julius Lacer, who worked in the provinces and built the famous Puente Alcantara in Spain.

Large bridges, like cathedrals, were not the inspiration of one man alone, and were generally products of whole communities that labored in building them for more than one generation.

During the Middle Ages the art of bridgebuilding was preserved by the Church. Monks of various ecclesiastic orders formed themselves into a brotherhood of bridgebuilders; and though they built a few new bridges, like the Pont d'Avignon, their principal work was maintaining and repairing the existing Roman bridges until the Renaissance. In the hands of Renaissance architectural designers and master masons, the simple Romanesque arch underwent a variety of changes. In the northern cathedrals it was elongated into the delicate, high, pointed Gothic arch supported by flying buttresses. As used in the building of bridges, its shape was altered in an opposite way. In order to allow a greater span, the bridge arch was widened and flattened, thus losing its classic semicircular shape. The structural principles that made it self-supporting, of course, remained the same.

The Rialto Bridge in Venice is an excellent example of a Renaissance stone-arch bridge and, as you see in Figure 1, or—better still—as you pass under it today in a gondola, you will notice that the arch is no longer a complete half-circle, but instead is a part, or segment, of a much larger arc. This span, three times the length of those on the Pons Augustus, crosses the 90-foot width of the Grand Canal in one leap. During the construction of this famous bridge the whole project was nearly undermined by a whispering campaign to the effect that such a novel design was unsafe, and only after the bridge had withstood an earthquake was its builder, Antonio da Ponte (Anthony Bridge), hailed as a great engineer.

Andrea Palladio's design (Figure 2) is a variation on the Pons Augustus, which Palladio very much admired, but again the length of arch has been doubled. The three arches that carried the Santa Trinita Bridge across the Arno at Florence (Figure 3) were elliptical in shape. The unusual curve of these graceful arches becomes less mysterious when one realizes that the bridge's engineer, Ammanati, called in no less an artist than

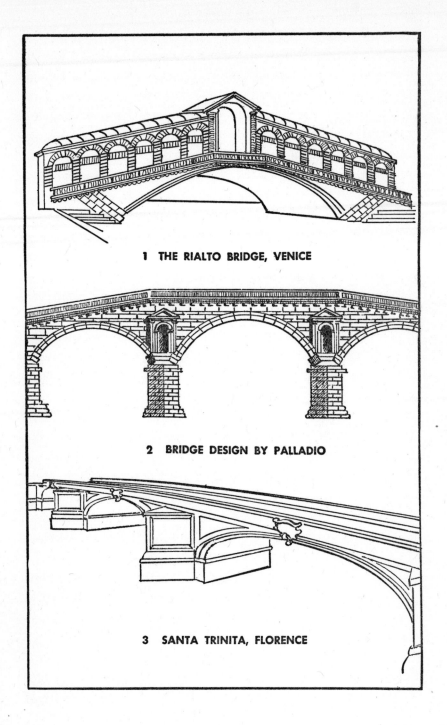

1 THE RIALTO BRIDGE, VENICE

2 BRIDGE DESIGN BY PALLADIO

3 SANTA TRINITA, FLORENCE

Michelangelo to help in drawing the design. Unfortunately this beautiful bridge was destroyed in World War II.

At the beginning of the eighteenth century the French government set up a commission to pass on all plans for bridges, roads, and canals. Some years later the first engineering school in the world, known as the Ecole des Ponts et Chaussées, was established in Paris. Here for the first time technical knowledge was shared and studied, with the result that in the second half of that century masonry bridges were brought to their greatest perfection.

First Jacques Gabriel in the seventeenth century and then Jean Perronet in the eighteenth became the master bridge-builders of France. The latter's bridge across the Seine at Neuilly (below) was recognized as a remarkable piece of engineering as well as one of the most beautiful stone bridges in France. Each of the five arches has a 120-foot span, while the piers that support them are only 13 feet thick. It is the lightness of these piers in relation to the length of span that makes this bridge a masterpiece of masonry construction. As you see, the bridge resembles a series of flying buttresses that, anchored to the heavy abutments at each end, carry the thrust of the bridge from one arch to the next. Here at last was a series of arches that allowed the water to flow underneath with minimum resistance; in comparison, the Pons Augustus gives the appearance of a solid rampart.

In Perronet's Neuilly bridge the self-supporting stone arch reached a final stage of perfection; stones and mortar have never been made to soar more lightly and gracefully across a natural obstacle.

It was not until the end of the eighteenth century that iron was first used in Europe as a bridgebuilding material. The English were the great master ironworkers of the Industrial Revolu-

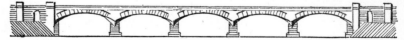

tion, and it was natural that engineers in England such as Thomas Telford and Marc Isambard Brunel should be among the first to use iron in building bridges. Sixty years before the United States Army engineers finished the iron bridge at Brownsville, Pennsylvania, a semicircular iron-arch bridge had been erected across the Severn at Coalbrookdale, England. The structural members or sections of these first iron bridges were made of cast iron, which is far more brittle than wrought iron and does not have the latter's strength under tension. The bridge at Coalbrookdale is still in use, but this is due in part to the fact that its traffic today is limited to light, slow, horse-drawn vehicles. From the bridge engineer's point of view the possibilities of these new processed materials were immense, but hardly had they begun their experimentation when that other product of the iron age, the steam locomotive, appeared on the scene. Here was a "live load" that moved four times as fast and, even at the start, weighed five times as much as anything that they had had to cope with before. It was not an easy problem to solve.

The stone arches and wooden bridges of the National Pike might have carried the B & O's little "Tom Thumb" engine traveling at fifteen miles an hour, but by the time the tracks had been laid to Wheeling the company's new locomotives weighed twenty-five tons and hauled their train of cars at forty miles an hour.

The wagon bridges on the old pike could not have withstood the racking vibration caused by such a moving load. Also, wooden trestles never lasted very long, for sooner or later a spark from the firebox would touch them off. From here on the history of bridges in the United States is a dual history, one aspect having to do with the constant change in methods of construction as new materials were introduced, and the other with the ever-increasing weight and speed of the loads they had to carry.

From 1850 on, the network of rails spread out across the

country with the speed of an animated cartoon. Each year the web of connecting lines between the commercial and industrial centers filled more of the map. The future prosperity of villages, towns, and cities hung in the balance until they were sure that they were on the main line of the railroad. The need for all-metal bridges kept the foundries going day and night. Their products were strictly utilitarian, standard, iron truss bridges, undistinguished as to span length, commonplace as to engineering design, and, to the layman's eye, all equally ugly. Many of these metal truss bridges still mar the landscape and, if we notice them at all today, it is only as homely reminders of the great days of railroading when even on the single-track spur lines there were four trains a day, all crowded.

In 1847 a civil engineer named Squire Whipple published a theoretical treatise on the structural principles of truss bridges. Whipple was among the first to use exact mathematical calculations in determining the stresses and strains that metal bridges had to stand. After many years as a bridge designer for the Baltimore and Ohio, he retired to Utica, New York, where he made mathematical and "philosophical" instruments. Whipple patented a standard, bowstring, overhead truss bridge (shown below) for spans of less than 200 feet. He made careful tests of the relative strength of cast iron as compared to wrought iron, and as a result his bridge was a practical combination of both.

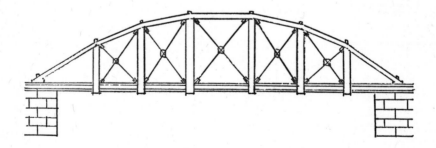

Only the upper bowstring section of his bridge was made of cast iron—all the rest being wrought iron. Thousands of bridges of this design were built throughout the country to carry the relatively light railroad trains of that day. This same type of bridge was used for highway traffic later and well into the present century; even now, there are many county roads that still depend on an old, rusty, Whipple-truss bridge, marked with a large sign: "Load Limit 5 Tons."

During the Civil War, every bridge across the Tennessee between Knoxville and the Ohio was blown up, and wholesale destruction occurred in many other river valleys. After the war there was a second boom in railroad expansion, and the general need for cheap, practical bridges led to the designing and patenting of cast-iron bridges like the Pratt truss (Figure 1) and the Fink truss (Figure 2). During that period it became the custom for the railroads to order their bridges directly from the foundries, accepting the specifications that these commercial companies recommended. The competition was brisk and price

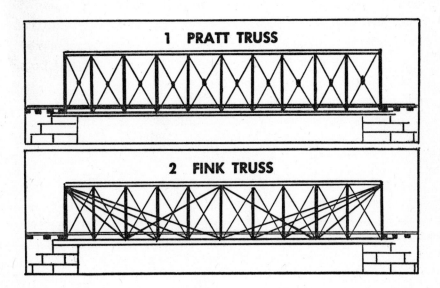

1 PRATT TRUSS

2 FINK TRUSS

cutting on standard, patented bridges was the order of the day. Twenty years before, Squire Whipple had pointed out that for its cost "cast iron will resist a crushing force better than any other substance . . ." But he also went on to say that, though wrought iron was twice as expensive, it had four times the tensile strength, or resistance to being pulled apart, of cast iron. Despite these warnings the cheaper material was used, while at the same time the span length of these cast-iron bridges was almost doubled.

So much for the materials used in the "iron age," but in following the dual history of bridgebuilding one must note the enormous increase in the weight and speed of what engineers refer to as "railroad loadings." In 1831 the New York Central's crack locomotive, the "DeWitt Clinton," weighed no more than 3½ tons. Sixty years later the standard freight or passenger engine, with its loaded tender, pounded across the truss bridges with a total weight of between 70 and 80 tons, unevenly distributed along 50 feet of track. The greatest change in the weight of locomotives occurred between 1870 and 1890, during which time the dead weight of the engine doubled. By comparison the change in speed was negligible. The end result of the presence of these moving forces on the long-span, cast-iron bridges caused the failure of two hundred and fifty-one railroad bridges within a ten-year period.

At first, people in the United States paid little attention to the collapse of a bridge here and there. They were used to seeing them washed away, blown down, or burned up, and the frightful destruction during the Civil War only added to people's indifference. However, when the Lake Shore's special limited, "Number Five," crashed through the Ashtabula bridge in Ohio on a snowy night in December 1877, killing ninety persons, the whole country was shocked into the recognition that far too many of its railroad bridges were defective. There had been the failure of the Norfolk and Western's Big Otter Bridge, only to

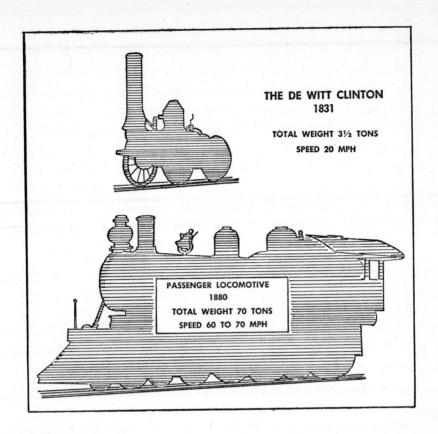

THE DE WITT CLINTON
1831

TOTAL WEIGHT 3½ TONS
SPEED 20 MPH

PASSENGER LOCOMOTIVE
1880
TOTAL WEIGHT 70 TONS
SPEED 60 TO 70 MPH

be followed by the loss of fourteen lives in the Chester Bridge disaster on the Boston and Albany line. An 80-ton locomotive wrecked the Big Otter Bridge over the Illinois River at Peoria, and early-morning commuters going into Boston were unceremoniously dumped in the streets of Dedham when the "tin" Chester Bridge at Busey Avenue gave way. The aroused press and citizens angrily demanded a complete investigation into the causes of these disasters. There were many careful inquiries into the problem, and one weary engineer, after a thorough inspection of the bridges along a section of right of way, ended his report as follows: ". . . finally, I can see no engineering reason for this bridge standing at all, except it be—from force of habit."

The public's indignation and well-founded anxiety as to the safety of rail travel did bring results. The railroads set themselves the program of replacing the old, obsolete structures and agreed to build no more cast-iron bridges. Wrought-iron trusses were still used, but they were no longer bought by the dozen from competing bridge-fabricating companies. Instead the railroads turned to those civil engineers who had had experience as bridgebuilders. Independent engineering firms now acted as consultants and took on the professional responsibility of building sound structures. As techniques for testing materials improved, more exact specifications were drawn up, and rigid standards of design and methods of construction were carried out without commercial interference. Mathematical theory, which for some time had been part of the European engineers' training, began to replace the old rule-of-thumb methods.

As a result of these changes, the bridge engineer, though still within the general category of civil engineers, became more and more a specialist in the designing of metal structures. There was no thought that the weight and speed of railroad trains must be curtailed to meet the load limitations as set by existing bridges. In fact as more and more safety requirements were placed on our railroads, the trains became heavier and the locomotives even larger. Ten years after the Ashtabula disaster, the new, eighty-ton, twelve-wheeled, Pacific-type locomotives were already becoming dangerous burdens for even our best wrought-iron bridges. It then became the problem of the bridge engineer to fashion a structure that could withstand the pounding of their heavy drivers going fifty miles an hour. Of course the only possible answer was again the use of a new material, this time structural steel.

The strength and toughness of steel had been known for centuries, but up to the middle of the nineteenth century steel was so costly to produce that it could be used only for sharp-edged tools. In the 1860s, through the inventive genius of English and

European metallurgists, steel was produced in sufficient quantities to make its use economically practical in the building of metal structures. Within a decade the United States was producing a million tons of steel each year and our bridge engineers were quick to see the possibilities offered by this light material which had a working strength twenty per cent greater than that of wrought iron. The two well-known pioneers in the use of steel in bridge construction were James Buchanan Eads and John Roebling. Eads built an epoch-making steel-arch bridge across the Mississippi at St. Louis and Roebling his world-famous suspension bridge over New York's East River. Roebling's Brooklyn Bridge will be taken up later, for it is not strictly a railroad bridge, whereas the Eads Bridge at St. Louis, though it carried vehicles on its upper deck, was designed to carry the heaviest railroad loadings of that period, and even today modern Diesels pass over its three arches with complete safety.

The Mississippi River played an important part in making St. Louis the gateway to the West. Also, because the city grew up on the west bank, the river effectively cut it off from direct overland communication with the East. The need for a bridge was soon evident, and Colonel Charles Ellet, the dauntless conqueror of the Ohio, was the first engineer to submit plans for overcoming the "father of waters." In his judgment this could easily be accomplished merely by enlarging the proportions of his Wheeling suspension bridge. But no matter how great the need for a bridge into Illinois might be, the mayor and his advisers, after going over the plans, saw at once that Ellet had no conception of the behavior of the Mississippi and had woefully underestimated its power.

The Missouri River enters the Mississippi some twenty miles upstream from St. Louis, and it is in part responsible for the unpredictable 41-foot rise and fall between high and low water. Where the river flows past the city it is about 1500 feet wide, and its rock bed varies in depth, being in some places as much as 136 feet below high water. Shifting sand and silt are continuously being deposited on this rock bed, but every so often, during flood periods, the turbulent water will scour the rocks clean, carrying all the deposit downstream to form new sand bars and shallow backwaters. In winter, grinding ice floes pile up to a depth of twenty feet, often making it impossible for boats to cross for weeks at a time. Violent as the Ohio may be, it bears little comparison to the wild and temperamental monster that glides past St. Louis. This indeed was a natural barrier of the first order, and to bridge it required not only great determination but constant watchfulness born from knowledge of its swiftly changing moods.

Captain Eads knew the river well. He had begun his engineering career salvaging sunken river steamers, so his knowledge extended to what went on at the bottom of the river as well as on the surface. In the summer of 1867, after the political and financial wrangling that always precedes the actual start of bridge construction, Eads submitted his final proposals. His report explained that the superstructure of the bridge would take the form of three steel arches, the middle one being 520 feet in length and the others 502. The ribs of these arches would be made of hollow steel tubing, strong enough to carry two railway tracks on the lower deck and highway traffic on the upper. This was not an all-steel bridge, for the plans specified wrought-iron supports and framing above the arches. Eads went on to say that he planned to build his own testing machine and that all metal sections used in the bridge had to meet the standards that had been established. In referring to the masonry foundations for the bridge, Eads carefully described the river bed and the scouring action of the water, concluding as follows: ". . . for these reasons I have maintained and urged that there is no safety short of resting the piers of your Bridge firmly on the rock itself."

Earlier this bridge was referred to as "epoch-making"; today's

engineers agree that Eads' pioneer work on the St. Louis bridge set the pattern for modern methods of bridge construction. Placing the foundations on the bedrock meant working at greater depths under more severe conditions than had ever before been attempted. The span of the steel arches was 200 feet greater than any that had yet been built. The processes for manufacturing structural steel were still experimental, and the techniques for testing this new material and calculating its working strength were entirely theoretical. In the light of today's specialized knowledge, Eads' accomplishment was indeed remarkable, for he had to be his own consulting specialist in matters of geology and metallurgy, in the analysis of materials and the estimation of the forces they could withstand, and in the use of compressed-air caissons and pneumatic equipment that had never before been used in this country. He had no well-trained staff of experienced engineers to help him, and so, during the seven years that it took to build the bridge, Eads found himself solely responsible not only for the design and construction of the bridge but also for a series of experimental

another two hours of slow decompression to free his tissues
of the excess nitrogen he had absorbed under this pressure. It
was a tragic lesson, a problem for which there was no answer
at that time, and it was many years before men were again
asked to work at such depths.

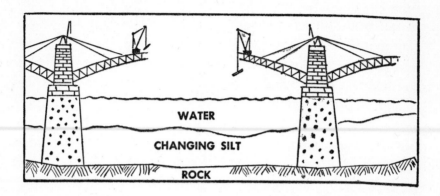

To build a wooden form, or what is known as "falsework,"
for the erection of the steel arches would, of course, have been
impossible under the circumstances. Eads carried out the erection of the arches by means of the cantilever method illustrated
in the diagram above. During the attempt to close the first arch
another great difficulty arose. This crucial situation occurred in
September, when the heat of the sun had so expanded the steel
tubes that formed the ribs of the arch that the gap left for the
last section was too small to receive it. To wait for cool autumn
weather was impossible, for the contract called for the completion of the arch by September 19, and failure to carry this
through might jeopardize a half-million-dollar loan needed to
finish the bridge. Special crews were called in, wooden troughs
were hung under the arch ribs, and the whole arch was packed
with sixty tons of ice. The shrinkage, however, was not enough.
Finally, two days before the contract expired, by readjusting
the cantilever cables and tightening the steel tubes already in
place, the workers were able to fit the last section into position

and closed the arch after sixty-five hours of continuous work.

This grueling job was carried out by a young assistant engineer, Theodore Cooper, who, when it was over, reported to Eads, "We were so sleepy that it was almost impossible to keep our eyes open and I was much afraid that some of us would fall into the river." No one knew better than Cooper what it meant to fall from the superstructure into the Mississippi, for only a few months before, he had missed his footing on a loose plank and plummeted ninety feet to the water. It is reported that during the fall he rapidly calculated the force with which he would strike the water, while, at the same time, he had the presence of mind to roll himself into a ball. It was a deep plunge, but when he came to the surface he struck out for the rowboat that had already pushed off to pick him up. When he was hauled in, he found he was still clutching his pencil, and half an hour later, after a change of clothes, he was back on the bridge, supervising the work.

Once the steel arches were joined, the rest of the work on the superstructure of the bridge moved ahead swiftly. The formal opening took place on the Fourth of July, 1874, when the whole town turned out to celebrate not only the independence of the United States, but also its own new independence from the Mississippi as a barrier to the East. All day, long processions led by brass bands marched back and forth, but the most dramatic and reassuring feature of the day was a parade of fourteen of the heaviest locomotives of that time moving slowly across the river. A few years later, thanks to the bridge, St. Louis became one of the largest rail centers in the Middle West. Besides having served its community for over eighty years, the Eads Bridge now stands as an important landmark in the history of bridgebuilding, for it ushered in the age of steel and, along with it, the reliance on exact mathematical calculation, the analysis and testing of materials, and the modern techniques of bridge construction.

V. New Shapes in Steel

AS ONE studies the early history of bridgebuilding in this country, it becomes clear that, though our engineers strove to build structures that would last, their efforts were not always successful. All too often they were forced to stand by helplessly and watch their bridges being swept away by floods or blown down by tornadoes, or crashing in flames among rising clouds of steam and smoke as glowing timbers plunged into the river. For the most part, the bridges that remain today, whether they be short-span stone bridges, covered timber bridges, or iron trusses, are little more than curiosities that stand forsaken on old roads long since bypassed by new expressways. However, when one remembers that there were greater changes in the art of bridgebuilding in the nineteenth century than in the twenty centuries that preceded it, and that only after the introduction of structural steel could bridge spans be first doubled and then tripled, it is little wonder that rural bridges look old-fashioned.

The forces of nature that can wreck a bridge usually work on two levels; those below water level attack the substructure, and those above, the superstructure. Besides floods and the continuous erosive action of flowing water, the piers and abutments of the substructure can be destroyed by the action of ice and by earthquakes or the shifting of the bed strata under the foundations. The superstructure is constantly endangered by its own dead weight, by wind, snow, and violent temperature changes. The impact of a hundred-ton locomotive traveling at sixty miles an hour, as well as the mere rhythm of marching men, can set up vibrations that will rack the structure apart. How to meet these dangers became the secrets of the master bridgebuilder. He relied on tradition and judged the quality of his materials and the stability of his structural design more by

53

instinct and personal experience than by any objective system of standards.

Bridgebuilders like Eads and Roebling led the way in the establishment of just such a system of engineering standards. As a result of their methods, the designing and construction of bridges lost all resemblance to a craft and became a highly specialized, technical profession. From then on it was customary for each engineer to prepare thorough studies and reports covering all aspects of his proposed bridge. These "engineering considerations" finally came to include not only the design for the bridge and the plans for its construction, but everything from the way in which the project would be financed to the attempt to estimate the amount of traffic that would use the bridge ten years later.

As bridges grew, both in span length and in height, the placing of the piers and abutments on solid rock became an absolute necessity. Today the substructure of a bridge often represents more than half its cost. Once the bridge site has been chosen, deep borings are taken in order to locate a rock strata strong enough to resist the downward pressure of the bridge. On this point geologists may be called in as consultants. All information as to the character and behavior of the river is taken into account—its maximum rise and fall, its speed of flow, ice conditions, and so on. The foundations of the Brooklyn Bridge lie 78 feet below high water, while Eads, as we have seen, had to work at a depth of more than 100 feet to strike rock under the Mississippi. Not all bridges require such deep foundations, but in the course of recent years, through special methods and devices, piers have been founded at 240 feet below the surface. Today some construction firms specialize in the use of compressed-air caissons, and the old hazards of working under compressed air have been controlled. Another great step forward was the introduction of a cement that would set under water. This in turn was followed by the extensive use of reinforced concrete, which meant that the old master stonemasons were replaced by experts in the erection of man-made masonry.

It is difficult to remember that steel as a structural material has been used by only three generations of engineers, so that it is a novelty compared to wood and stone. Steel has two important virtues as a bridgebuilding material; in relation to its weight it is stronger than any other, and it has unusual tensile strength. Steel is also more elastic than iron, wood, or stone and as a result can better withstand the effects of impact and vibration. A bridge's own weight (dead load) puts all its members under constant stress, and the presence of heavy moving loads on its deck increases and intensifies these stresses. The correct measurement of these strains and stresses on a bridge structure can be arrived at only through a series of complicated mathematical calculations. Going a step farther, it is evident that these estimates are valuable to a bridge designer only if he is working with a structural material whose strength is known and whose quality is uniform. Thus the bridge engineer has had to become not only a mathematician but also a metallurgist. Eads had great difficulty in procuring a uniform quality of steel even though the commercial fabricators were already turning out a million tons a year. Today that figure has jumped to fifty million, and the annual production now includes half a dozen kinds of structural steel that can meet the most rigid tests for strength and uniformity.

Steel and mathematics have made it possible for engineers to design and build bridges whose span length and carrying capacity far exceed even the most optimistic prophecies of seventy-five years ago. The permanence of steel bridges as compared to that of many ancient stone-arch bridges has still to be proved, but the evidence so far indicates that they will endure for long periods. The strength and rigidity of steel in relation to its dead weight is an important factor in this consideration. Metal rusts, and this corrosion is a constant threat to

the life of steel bridges, but can be controlled by constant re-
painting. The old hazard of fire has been eliminated and temperature changes are taken care of through specially devised expansion joints. As I have mentioned earlier, the effect of high
winds on long-span bridges, particularly suspension bridges, has
been hard to gauge; only recently, through the testing of model
bridges in wind tunnels, have we begun to understand the
aerodynamic forces that can tear a bridge apart.

Changes in bridge design, like those in architecture, evolve
slowly; the work of Eads and Roebling did not have its full
effect until the turn of the century. In the meantime, the knowledge and experience acquired in building the iron truss bridges
for the railroads proved to be valuable training for the bridge
engineer. True, the widespread failure of railway bridges in
the 1870s was a costly form of experimentation, yet these
wrecked bridges clearly proved the weakness of the designs
of that period. Later, when the younger engineers, such as
Theodore Cooper and others who had worked under Eads and
Roebling, came to set up their own firms, they were equipped
to meet the challenge of building long-span steel bridges. Very
naturally this demand brought forth new designs, which took
the form of steel arches, massive cantilever bridges, and finally
the modern suspension bridge. All these steel shapes rose more
or less simultaneously during the first decade of the twentieth
century, but for the sake of clarity each of these new bridge
forms will be dealt with under separate headings.

Steel Arches

Long before Eads drew his plans for the St. Louis bridge,
the use of the arch shape in designing metal bridges was familiar
to many engineers. Eads' originality lay in daring to propose an
arch built of tubular steel ribs with a span length of 500 feet.
His structure proved that steel arches of this size were entirely

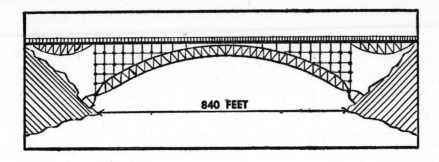

840 FEET

practical and could carry the heaviest railroad loadings. Even
to the most critical modern eye the three flattened arches of
Eads' bridge have a simplicity that was far ahead of the heavy,
complicated truss designs of that period.

One of the longest steel-arch bridges of the late nineteenth
century was built over the Niagara River, just below the falls,
and was very appropriately known as the "Honeymoon Bridge"
(see above). The span of this arch was 840 feet; its two ends
were anchored to the abutments by means of heavy steel castings. These castings took the form of hinges, which in engineering terms made the bridge a "two-hinged arch," whereas in the
Eads Bridge the "fixed-end arches" rest directly on the piers.
From the day that Colonel Ellet drew the first steel cable across
the gorge, the Niagara River has been a challenge to bridgebuilders. As we saw in Chapter III, John Roebling replaced
Ellet's footbridge with a suspension bridge strong enough to
carry the railroad trains of that day, and this in turn was super-
seded by the simple steel arch of the "Honeymoon Bridge."

This new bridge was put to a severe test during the first winter
after its completion. Due to unusually cold weather a great ice
dam formed just below the falls and raised the water level above
it twenty feet. When this ice barrier finally gave way with a
splintering crash, the whole mass swirled downstream, tear-
ing at the abutments and hinged ends of the arch. The bridge
shuddered. Everyone thought that it would go, but the steel

castings held and the churning mountains of ice were split apart as they swept down the gorge. But the Niagara River had given its warning, and forty years later, in the winter of 1938, a similar ice barrier threw itself upon the bridge and damaged it beyond repair.

Before the Hell Gate Bridge was built there was no direct rail link between New England and the Middle Atlantic states. Passengers traveling between Washington and Boston had to change trains in New York City and freight cars were barged across the Hudson from the old Pennsylvania terminal to the Manhattan side. The Hell Gate arch carries four heavily ballasted tracks and was built only for railroad use. When completed in 1916 it was the longest arch span in the world—977 feet.

Its designer, Gustav Lindenthal, came to this country as a young engineer shortly after the St. Louis bridge had been completed. One could say that Lindenthal grew up with steel and that his long and brilliant career as a bridgebuilder found its fullest expression in this monumental arch that bestrides Hell Gate. Across the narrow channel where the tides of Long Island Sound and those of the East River meet in treacherous whirlpools, Lindenthal erected the world's strongest long-span bridge.

After eighty years in which bridgebuilders had tried to keep pace with the ever-increasing weight of railway traffic, this heavy steel structure might well be considered as a kind of triumphal arch, for it marks a high point in railroad-bridge engineering. The Hell Gate arch was designed to carry any load that could move on tracks and crossties. For years now it has withstood the vibrations and terrific impact caused by the lurching and rocking of the 200-ton Diesels or electric locomotives that thunder across its suspended roadway at sixty miles an hour. It is almost impossible to gauge the ultimate strength of a bridge. Engineers simply refer to the "designed carrying capacity" of a bridge, which is usually given as a figure representing the number of pounds that a structure will safely support per lineal foot of the span. The carrying capacity of the Hell Gate arch is set at 76,000 pounds per lineal foot, 52,000 representing the average dead weight of the bridge itself and 24,000 the maximum moving live load that can cross it with safety.

As one glides across this bridge in a streamlined coach, or views it from the nearby Triborough Bridge, it is almost impossible to get any idea of its scale or magnitude. The four end-sections of the lower chord of the arch weigh 185 tons each and still hold the record of being the biggest and heaviest single steel members ever used in the construction of a bridge. As you can see from the drawing, the two chords of the arch are braced in the usual N-shaped manner. During construction, each half of the arch was built out from the base of the towers, and until joined, each was supported by heavy backstays temporarily anchored behind the massive piers. The most powerful hydraulic jacks then in existence were held in readiness to help in closing the arch. However, when the ends met in the air, 300 feet above the racing tides, it required an adjustment of only five-sixteenths of an inch to bring them into line! How was it possible to fabricate 40 million tons of steel into the separate members that made up the bridge and, after fitting them together, to end with such a small fractional discrepancy? This remarkable achievement was due to the care and precision used not only throughout the period of construction but also during the laborious earlier months of planning and designing, when every part of the bridge was subjected to the most minute and detailed mathematical calculation and analysis.

The Hell Gate arch was completed in 1916, but its carrying capacity in relation to its span length still makes it the veritable Atlas of steel bridges. Fifteen years later the longest single steel arch in the world was opened across the Kill van Kull waterway that separates Staten Island from the New Jersey mainland. This arch, known as the Bayonne Bridge, was built by the Port of New York Authority as a vehicular bridge with a span length of 1652 feet. The designer of this bridge, O. H. Ammann (who later designed the George Washington Bridge) had worked as a young bridge engineer under Lindenthal during the planning and construction of the Hell Gate Bridge. The two steel arches are very similar in design except that the masonry towers were never completed on the Bayonne Bridge. Today, as one drives along the Jersey Turnpike, across the flat salt marshes below Newark, the dark, webbed crescent of this magnificent arch rises to the east like a perfectly rounded mountain above the smoky horizon.

The Hell Gate and the Bayonne Bridges mark the two extreme limits of existing steel arches—the first in carrying capacity, the second in span length. But between these extremes American

engineers have built many useful, economical, and at the same time handsome steel-arch bridges. In designing these bridges the question of whether the deck should pass through the arch and hang suspended below it, or should be placed above and rest on the arch is not merely a matter of preference but is generally determined by the bridge site itself. Where the bridge stands below the surrounding approaches, like the "Honeymoon Bridge," it is natural to design an open-deck bridge with the roadway running above the arch. The Henry Hudson Bridge that carries the West Side Highway from Manhattan to the Bronx across Spuyten Duyvil Creek is a fine example of this type of deck-arch bridge.

Four years after the "Honeymoon Bridge" was wrecked by ice in the Niagara River, the Rainbow Bridge (above) had taken its place. Though the older two-hinged, trussed arch was light and simple for its day, the one completed in 1941 is an outstanding achievement in modern design. In order to avoid the hazards of ice jams in the gorge, the builders set the abutments of the new bridge higher up on the steep banks of the river, thus extending the span length from 840 to 950 feet, which is only a bit shorter than the Hell Gate arch. Unlike the hinged ends of the older bridge, those of the Rainbow arch are fixed to the abutments, thus making it the longest fixed-end arch in the United States.

The designer of this bridge, Shortridge Hardesty, has had a full and successful career in the building of bridges in this country. His firm has built at least one of almost every type of existing steel bridge, and these are spotted from Maine to California. Perhaps only after a lifetime of working with structural steel can one dare to design an arch as clean, as graceful, and as utterly simple as this one. As the drawing shows, the ribs of

this arch do not have the usual upper and lower chords with N-bracing between. Instead, the sections that make up the arch are fashioned in the form of hollow boxes (known as box girders) 12 feet deep and 140 feet long. With these sections joined together the unbroken line of this crescent-shaped girder seems to spring lightly and gracefully from one side of the gorge to the other. The Rainbow Bridge is in perfect keeping with the dramatic landscape that surrounds it.

The erection of this bridge is remarkable in many ways, but above all for the extensive and thorough safety precautions taken throughout the period of its construction. From prehistoric times onward, the building of bridges has been recognized as a highly dangerous occupation. Undoubtedly these dangers played a part in the ancient superstition that the river gods were angry and would destroy the bridge unless placated by a human sacrifice. Later there was the saying, "Every bridge demands at least one life," and unfortunately this did seem to be proved with terrible regularity. The deck or roadway of the Rainbow arch crosses the gorge almost 200 feet above the surface of the river. From the start of construction right through to the final coat of paint, safety nets were slung under the ribs of the arch. These nets caught five workmen. The engineer's report on the safety procedures ends as follows: "It should be noted that all erection work on the structure including the concrete deck was completed without a single fatality or a single serious injury."

Engineers now set a limit on the span length of steel arches at approximately 2000 feet. It is entirely possible that within the next decade the record span of the Bayonne Bridge will be surpassed. On the other hand it is difficult to conceive of any arch or other bridge design in which steel could be used with greater economy, engineering ingenuity, or simple beauty than the way in which it has been fashioned to support the Rainbow arch over the Niagara River.

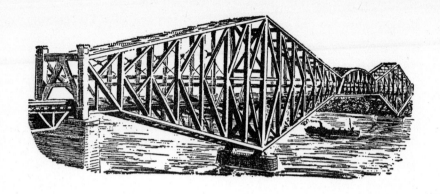

Cantilever Bridges

Like the steel arch, the cantilever bridge came into being as an answer to the railroads' need for long-span bridges that could carry heavier moving loads. As steel structures began to replace the old wrought-iron railway trusses, bridge engineers found that the strength and lightness of this new material allowed them to lengthen the truss without the usual loss in carrying capacity. A steel cantilever bridge is a form of elongated truss balanced in such a way that its arms extend three to four times as far as the old diagonally braced Fink or Pratt truss of the 1860s. England led the way in the designing of cantilever bridges with the successful construction of the gigantic Firth of Forth Bridge, which was completed in 1889.

Our first attempts to build big cantilever bridges in this country and Canada were plagued with difficulties. Construction on the Quebec Bridge (above) across the St. Lawrence River was started in 1904, but this all-steel cantilever structure was not completed until fourteen years later, after taking the lives of more than eighty men and ruining the career of Theodore Cooper, who by then had become one of our foremost bridge designers. As you remember, Cooper survived his ninety-foot fall into the Mississippi, but when a large section of the uncompleted superstructure of the Quebec Bridge collapsed into the

St. Lawrence, so did Cooper's professional reputation. This disaster occurred in 1907 during the construction of one of the arms of the cantilever that stretched out toward midstream. The other end of the steel web had been firmly attached to its pier anchorage on the bank, but as the heavy derrick and its assembly crew moved out to the last completed section, the lower chord of the cantilever began to buckle, and in a matter of seconds 9000 tons of steel crashed into the river, carrying all but eleven of the crew with it.

A long and thorough investigation generally follows a disaster of such magnitude; in the course of it many problems of design and construction are critically reappraised. Naturally the general public held Theodore Cooper—as chief engineer of the project—to blame, whereas most bridge engineers recognized that this catastrophe was not a matter of negligence. As the inquiry dragged on, it became clear that the failure of the bridge, like other ventures into the unknown, had been caused by physical factors (stresses and strains) which as yet lay beyond the possibility of exact mathematical calculation. But Quebec still needed a railroad bridge and the width of the St. Lawrence River did not change. As a result of the inquiry, new designs and new methods of erection were planned. This time, instead of attempting to build the center truss by working outward from the cantilever arms until the span was closed, the builders completely assembled the central truss on a barge and then floated it into midstream before lifting it into position by hydraulic jacks.

The central truss weighed 5200 tons; it had to be lifted 150 feet, and the estimated time for this operation was set at ninety-six hours. The four corners of the truss were held in specially rigged slings or stirrups. Everything went smoothly for the first 12 feet of the lift when suddenly one of the stirrup castings broke and the 640-foot truss plunged into the river. This second disaster, in 1916, cost the lives of thirteen men and injured more

than a dozen. Two years later this operation was successfully carried out and Quebec finally got its railroad bridge.

The other early cantilever bridge that gave engineers a great deal of difficulty was New York's Queensboro Bridge. This vast conglomeration of metal was started in 1901 as a means of connecting Manhattan Island, Welfare Island (in the center of the East River), and the Borough of Queens on the opposite shore. Though engineers always refer to the Queensboro as a cantilever bridge, to the layman's eye it looks more like a clumsy suspension bridge supported by steel girders rather than by cables. Its two main spans that cross the two channels of the East River are undistinguished as to length; the complicated jumble of diagonal bracing spoils the long lines of the bridge; and the pointed turrets that crown the towers look like Victorian lightning rods. As originally planned, the bridge was to carry four tracks on its upper deck for trolleys and subway trains, but after the Quebec Bridge disaster it was found that the dead weight of the bridge was already so great that one set of tracks had to be eliminated. This made it necessary to build a subway tube under the East River at an additional cost to the city of four million dollars. For almost fifty years the Queensboro has carried a heavy load of traffic, and like anything that gives long and faithful service as the years go by, it has been forgiven for its ugliness and accepted for its usefulness.

For spans under 2000 feet the cantilever bridge has generally proved to be the most economical. This fact, and the fact that the cantilever can be adapted to meet a great variety of situations, have made it a very popular bridge design with engineers. In time, some of the more cumbersome and complicated systems of cross bracing were found unnecessary. But even when this network of extra steel is eliminated, the cantilever bridge remains essentially a form of truss, and by comparison rarely has the beauty and grace of the steel-arch or the suspension bridge.

Suspension Bridges

When completed, the Brooklyn Bridge, which still stands as solidly as ever, aroused greater popular acclaim than almost any other bridge except, perhaps, the ancient one of London, which, according to the jingle, was always falling down. The sweeping grandeur of the Brooklyn Bridge has been reproduced on millions of postcards, and these in turn have carried its fame to all corners of the earth. At the opening ceremonies, in the spring of 1883, this bridge was hailed as the "Eighth Wonder of the World," and for years to visit New York without seeing the bridge was an oversight far worse than missing an opportunity to go to the top of the Empire State Building today. There was a time when John Roebling, its designer, became a household name in the United States and, unlike the majority of bridge builders, he is still known to the school children of this country. It is often the case with legendary heroes that far more is attributed to them than they ever claimed. And so even today it might be well to point out that Roebling did not invent the suspension bridge any more than Eads invented the steel arch.

As indicated earlier, the suspension bridge is one of the oldest forms of bridges, and its basic principles were known to primitive man long before the stone-arch or the timber bridge. Up to the beginning of the nineteenth century there were no building materials that were light enough and at the same time strong enough to support such a span over a wide natural obstacle. Cast-iron chains beyond a certain length parted under their own weight, and not until processed wrought iron and woven wire cables came into general use did suspension bridges begin to replace those of stone and wood. And so it was not a matter of chance that the first manufacturer of wire cables in this country also became the designer and builder of the first modern suspension bridge. Roebling started life in America as a pioneer farmer, but soon lost interest. Once he had worked out a method of weaving wire cables on his unused meadows near Pittsburgh, he spent his life demonstrating the tensile strength of metal wire.

Roebling began testing the strength of his cables by hauling loaded canal boats over the mountains from one watershed to the next. After that he went on to prove that wire cables could support overhead viaducts or flumes filled with water. As an expert on erecting suspended structures, he was soon called in to consult on bridges and, as we have seen, he began by picking up the pieces of Colonel Ellet's most daring, if not quite successful, projects.

Roebling had the determination, patience, and organizing ability of the good construction engineer; at the same time, being a trained mathematician, he was capable of working out the theoretical problems of bridge designing. But more important still, Roebling had the prophetic vision and unswerving conviction of the true innovator. These qualities stood him in good stead when the New York Bridge Commission asked him to prepare plans for a new bridge across the East River to Brooklyn.

Despite the fact that Roebling had designed and personally supervised the construction of the three longest suspension bridges in the country, New Yorkers were shocked to learn that he proposed to build a bridge with a span length of 1600 feet. Such a span would be half again as long as that of the Cincinnati Bridge across the Ohio, which he had just completed. It took all of Roebling's confidence and self-assurance to convince these officials, after months of indecision, that his plans were safe, practical, and economical. In May 1867 Robeling was appointed chief engineer for the project.

Actual work on the Brooklyn Bridge did not begin until two years later, and it was another fourteen years before the bridge was completed. During this long construction period there were many years that were filled with disappointment and heartbreak for those who labored on this monumental structure. Inevitably the bridge took many lives, but one of the earliest and most tragic was the death of Roebling in 1869. His foot had been crushed by a ferry boat while he was surveying the site for the Brooklyn pier, and he died of blood poisoning. His son, Washington Roebling, who for years had worked shoulder to shoulder with his father, was appointed by the bridge commission to act as chief engineer. Nearly every conceivable difficulty occurred during the placing of the foundations on which the two great masonry towers were to rest. Though the pneumatic caissons did not have to go to quite the same depth as those used by Eads, there were more than a hundred serious cases of the "bends" before the underwater work was completed. Also there were compressed-air leaks in the caissons, causing "blowouts" that shot huge geysers of mud, fog, and water into the air; there were fires in the working chamber, one of which necessitated the complete flooding of the caisson; there were labor troubles,

financial crises, and finally the physical breakdown of young
Roebling himself. At a critical point in the excavation work,
after twelve consecutive hours in the compressed-air chamber,
Roebling was taken out unconscious. He remained an invalid
the rest of his life, carrying on his father's work from his bedside
in Brooklyn Heights. His apartment overlooked the bridge site,
and he spent hours inspecting the progress of the bridge through
a telescope.

It took more than five years to build the towers and prepare
the cable anchorages for the Brooklyn Bridge, and it was not
until 1876 that the first ropes were strung between the massive
pylons, whose Gothic arches are faced with Maine granite. First
a light footbridge was erected so that workmen could inspect
the thousands of parallel wires that would be hung between the
two anchorages. Next a continuous rope, very much like a ski
tow, was rigged on pulleys to haul the loops of wire from one
anchorage, up and over the towers, to the opposite anchorage
across the river (see diagram). For the next twenty-six months
these sheaves, carrying their loops of wire, rose like giant spi-
ders, one from the Brooklyn side, the other from Manhattan,
and, trailing their thin steel strands behind them, they passed
each other midway between the towers, 135 feet above the harbor craft plying up and down the East River.

When two hundred and eighty-six parallel wires had been
strung, workmen standing along the footbridge bound these
into a single strand with light wire. When nineteen strands had
been completed and each strand firmly attached to its shoe in
the anchorage, a special crew set to work to form the final cable.
The nineteen strands were squeezed under extreme pressure
into a compact cylinder which was then wrapped tightly with a
softer, galvanized wire. As you can see today, the cables on the
Brooklyn Bridge, like those on all the other suspension bridges
that have followed it, have the appearance of huge steel pipes.
Each of the four cables on the bridge measures almost 16 inches

The Brooklyn Bridge has 4 cables. Each cable has 19 strands. Each strand has 286 wires.

16 inches

All the parallel wires in one strand are connected to one shoe at each anchorage. The 19 strands are compacted under pressure into a cylindrical shape and then tightly wrapped with a lighter wire.

ROEBLING'S METHOD OF SPINNING WIRES

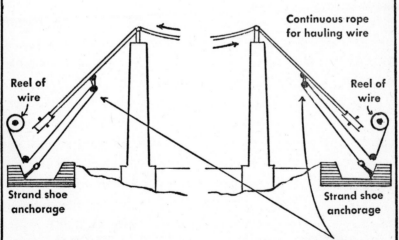

Continuous rope for hauling wire

Reel of wire

Reel of wire

Strand shoe anchorage

Strand shoe anchorage

The galvanized steel wire is looped around the traveling <u>sheave</u> or pulley. Each sheave moves back and forth, carrying the looped wire from anchorage to anchorage.

in diameter. Once the cables were in place the heavily braced platform or roadway was built out from each shore, section by section. Finally the diagonal "wind stays" were run up from the roadway to the top of the towers. It is these stays that give the bridge its weblike appearance.

Just as Eads led the way to the great steel arches that span our waterways today, so Roebling worked out the technical problems that have made it possible for us to build our modern long-span suspension bridges. The methods he developed for the erection and spinning of steel cables are still followed by bridge engineers. He predicted that steel cables fashioned in his manner could support a span of over 3000 feet, and in less than two generations the George Washington Bridge proved him correct. Roebling's other great contribution to the designing of suspension bridges was his insistence on adding a heavy stiffening truss below the suspended roadway. This truss served to distribute the weight of moving loads along the length of the bridge and, equally important, it helped to steady the bridge against the effects of strong winds. The success of the Brooklyn Bridge did much to overcome the skepticism of both the public and the engineering profession as regards the practicality and safety of suspension bridges. When asked by what means his bridges had proved more durable than those of other bridge engineers, Roebling said, "The means employed are: weight, girders, trusses and stays. With these any degree of stiffness can be insured to resist either the action of trains or the violence of storms."

For twenty years the Brooklyn Bridge held the record for length of span. Between 1900 and 1910 two more suspension bridges were built across the East River—first the Williamsburg and then the Manhattan. Though the span length of the Williamsburg is four feet greater than that of the Brooklyn, it never detracted from the fame and interest of the earlier bridge. These new structures followed Roebling's basic design, and the method of constructing the cables was the same. However, three things had been learned in the twenty-year period: first, that it was more economical to build the towers of structural steel rather than masonry; second, that the strength of the cold drawn wire for the cables had increased almost twenty-five per cent; third, that the stiffening trusses were sufficiently heavy to make the diagonal wind stays unnecessary.

The Manhattan Bridge, which was completed in 1909, was the first of the newer suspension bridges with only two cables. Another important improvement, on both the Williamsburg and Manhattan Bridges, was a marked reduction in construction time. Much of this saving took place in the erection of the steel towers, as well as in the spinning of the cables. To our modern eyes these towers appear clumsy and ornate, for they are decorated with moldings and cornices, and their metal spheres and fancy gewgaws give them the appearance of wrought-iron structures of the Civil War period. It is interesting to note that these three suspension bridges across the East River have undergone a careful inspection by Doctor David B. Steinman, one of the most prominent bridge engineers in this country. He found that the Brooklyn and the Williamsburg Bridges were sound throughout, though he recommended certain changes on the roadway of the Brooklyn Bridge. However, the youngest of the three, the Manhattan, has begun to show its age, and Doctor Steinman suggested the removal of two sets of elevated (now subway) tracks from its superstructure.

Until very recently long-span bridges were built to carry both rail and automobile traffic. The Quebec cantilever and the Hell Gate arch are exceptional bridges from this standpoint inasmuch as they were designed only for heavy railroad loadings. Most of the steel bridges in the late nineteenth and early twentieth centuries were built originally with one or two sets of tracks for interurban electric trains and trolleys, as well as vehicular traffic. In the 1930s, when buses replaced trolleys, the tracks were removed and the entire roadway of the bridge was turned over to automobile traffic. From then on, most of the longer-span bridges were designed solely to carry the increasing number of privately owned motorcars and buses and, as stated at the outset, these modern bridges are the particular concern of this book. The term "modern" as used here may be a bit confusing, for the Brooklyn Bridge, though over seventy years old, is still from an engineering point of view a modern bridge, especially when considered in relation to the long history of bridgebuilding. In the evolution of today's suspension bridges the periods of development overlap, and there is no single bridge that marks the beginning of the automobile era.

The Philadelphia–Camden Bridge, completed in 1926, is a good example of an intermediate stage in this development. For

a hundred years the patient citizens of Philadelphia and Camden depended on ferries to take them across the Delaware. After World War I this ferry traffic reached such proportions that the legislatures of Pennsylvania and New Jersey finally had to comply with the insistent popular demand for a bridge. The plans called for a suspension bridge with a span length of 1750 feet, which was 150 feet longer than the Williamsburg; though this set the world's record, the distinction lasted only a few years. However, there are certain innovations in the design of this bridge that later became standard engineering practice on many of the suspension bridges that were to follow.

The span of the Philadelphia–Camden Bridge is supported by only two cables, but these have almost twice the diameter of those on the Brooklyn Bridge. The spinning of the wires from one anchorage to the other was carried out in the same manner as on the earlier suspension bridges. However, once the parallel wires were in place a new method was used to squeeze the sixty-one strands into a single, compact cable. The hydraulic compressing device was placed around the strands of wire; under its total radial pressure of thirty tons to the square inch these strands were pressed into an almost solid steel cylinder 30 inches in diameter. The tensile strength of these cables far exceeded any that had preceded them.

The contrast in the design of the towers of this bridge with those of the twenty-years-older Manhattan Bridge indicate a radical change in the use of structural steel. The sections or members of the Philadelphia–Camden towers are fashioned like hollow boxes, being made of heavy steel plates riveted together to avoid buckling. These simplified forms, known as cellular steel construction, were developed after years of experimentation and were used for the first time on this bridge. The success of these massive towers pointed the way to those later designs that give functional dignity and grace to the great suspension bridges built during the next twenty years.

Concrete Bridges

The story of structural steel as a bridgebuilding material is not complete without some mention of the part that steel plays in reinforced and prestressed concrete bridges. Sand, gravel, Portland cement, and water, when mixed in the correct proportions, make the synthetic stone that we call "cement concrete." Like ordinary stone, long slabs of this man-made masonry will break under their own weight, for cement concrete is also lacking in tensile strength. If steel rods are embedded in the concrete, the natural tensile strength of the steel makes up for this deficiency and, when correctly combined, reinforces the concrete many times.

The combining of steel with concrete was not the bright idea of a bridge engineer, but that of a gardener. Less than a hundred years ago a Frenchman named Joseph Monier found that by inserting steel wires in the wet cement used for molding large flowerpots he made them less likely to crack. The evolution from Monier's flowerpots to the mammoth reinforced concrete arch of the Sando Bridge (Sweden), with its span length of 866 feet, was a matter of only seventy years. During those years it was the French, Swiss, and Scandinavian engineers who were the pioneers in perfecting methods for the building of reinforced-concrete structures. From 1900 on, the French have been the leaders in designing concrete bridges. There were two economic reasons for their interest in this new bridgebuilding material—

the relatively high cost of structural materials in Europe and the fact that highly skilled labor is far less expensive abroad than in the United States.

For years American bridge engineers have used reinforced concrete extensively in the building of towers, anchorages, and the approaches to their bridges, but not for the span itself. Recently, however, with the rapid expansion of express highways there was a need for thousands of short-span, over- or underpass bridges. As a result, our engineers came up with a standard, simplified form of reinforced-concrete span known as a "rigid frame" bridge (see page 151). Also, the highway departments of many states, particularly in the West, have experimented with medium-span concrete arches like the one shown below, which crosses Russian Gulch, near Fort Bragg, California. This delicate elliptical arch bears favorable comparison with the best reinforced-concrete bridges in Europe.

This is not the place for a detailed treatise on the latest developments in building prestressed concrete bridges. At present these new techniques are still being evaluated by the engineering profession. For our purpose it is enough to point out that prestressing concrete is for the most part a refinement of the

basic methods used in making reinforced concrete. Instead of embedding steel rods in the concrete, the bridge engineer uses steel wires stretched to a very high tension. The pull of these wires sets up a stress (in this case, compression) in that part of the concrete through which they run. It is this "locked in" prestress that is used to counteract the usual stresses caused by dead weight and live load (see pages 152–53). Again it has been the European bridgebuilders who are most interested in these new experimental techniques. So far the bridges built in this manner are lighter and more graceful than those of reinforced concrete, and again, though their construction requires expert workmanship, there is a considerable saving in structural materials.

The age of steel brought many changes, some in the form of wholly new creations, such as the airplane and the skyscraper, and others, such as the arch, the cantilever, and the long-span suspension bridges, which, though transformed to new and gigantic proportions, are actually the extensions of older shapes. Whether these bridge shapes be old or new, all are remarkable, and of them all the most astonishing is the modern suspension bridge. The austere beauty and revealed strength of these bridges are totally dependent on the inherent qualities of steel, and in them this structural material finds its fullest expression.

VI. The Automobile versus the Hudson River

AS MENTIONED earlier, the history of bridgebuilding in the United States is a dual history; one aspect deals with the changes and needs of an ever-expanding system of land transportation and the other with the development of bridge engineering in order to meet these needs. At the start wood and stone served well enough, when skillfully used, to carry the human foot and the horse-drawn vehicle over natural obstacles. However, as land transportation came to rely on sources of energy other than bone and muscle, the engineer had to devise longer and stronger bridges and so turned to the use of processed materials. Iron bridges carried the steam engine, and steel bridges now carry the gasoline engine.

For seventy years the demands of railroads set the pace for bridgebuilding. Though most of these bridges were made of short-span iron trusses, there were some that were remarkable for their total length. Supported by an almost endless number of piers, these structures marched across the widest of our mid-continental rivers. After Eads' St. Louis bridge was built, the

and farm produce were driven across the ice, followed by throngs of skaters, while iceboats cut in and out around the edges of the crowd.

Throughout the nineteenth century the ferry service improved, and there was hardly a ten-mile stretch that did not have at least one ferryboat plying back and forth at regular intervals. There are still those in the valley who remember the old horse-powered ferries. The motive power for these was furnished by two farm horses plodding on a sloping treadmill geared directly to the two crude paddlewheels. It was a slow trip across, and such a barge barely had enough headway to hold its own against the tide. Later on, from Manhattan Island northward, the steam-driven Hudson River ferryboats were quite capable of carrying all who wished to cross the river. However, before the turn of the century there were more customers than ferryboats on the half-dozen lines between downtown Manhattan and the Jersey shore. If the Pennsylvania Railroad had not put through its tunnels under the Hudson by 1910, the congestion at this point on the river might well have become a first-class bottleneck.

One of the first proposals for bridging the Hudson was made in 1811 by Thomas Pope, architect and landscape gardener. His "flying lever" bridge (opposite) was designed to connect New York and Hoboken. Pope's ambitious scheme never got farther than the model stage and a few lines of verse that began, "Let the broad arc, the spacious Hudson stride." From then on almost every bridgebuilder dreamed of conquering the mighty river. Ten years of acrimonious litigation passed before the first bridge was built at Albany just before the Civil War. One is likely to forget that from the start Albany was a seaport almost as important as New York. In the 1830s, after the opening of the Erie Canal, more than five hundred sailing vessels left that port each year bound for the West Indies and trade along the Atlantic coast. For its length and size the Hudson carried as heavy a load

of water-born traffic as any river in the country during the nineteenth century, and the idea of building a bridge that might
cause even a temporary interference with this commerce was
out of the question. Any structure that did not have a clearance
of at least 135 feet above high water would have been considered a threat to the economic life of the state. Even if such a
bridge could have been built it would have served only a small
number of horse-drawn vehicles and a few weary foot travelers
who much preferred a pleasant trip by ferry.

The railway bridge at Poughkeepsie was not built to meet the
transportation needs of that community or of those on the opposite bank. It was strictly a railroad promotion scheme by which
the factories of New England might be supplied with cheap
coal. This high, spindly, five-span, cantilever truss was to be a vital and direct link between the coal fields of Pennsylvania and
Boston. After two false starts and twelve years of stock juggling,
the bridge was finally completed in 1888, but for years the
freight traffic that it carried fell far short of expectations. Though
the local citizens still used the ferry to cross the river, the railroad bridge proved to be a fine vantage point from which to
watch the oarsmen sweeping down the river to the finish line in
the annual Hudson Regatta.

Until the First World War most of the travelers in the Hudson

Valley, whether they went by boat, rail, or automobile, moved up and down its length rather than across it. The steady customers for the steam ferries came from the sleepy towns and villages along the shore, and there were many months of the year when the little boats pushed back and forth on their hourly trips almost empty. Then in the early 1920s, without announcement or proclamation, the Fords, the Chevrolets, the Buicks—the "tin lizzies" of the period—began to swarm over the narrow macadam roads as they made their week-end tours up the valley. This did not happen in one year or two, but, like the salt tides that make the Hudson brackish as far north as Kingston, this automotive infiltration spread from the metropolitan area up along both banks, and what before had been a pleasant summer crowd at the ferry landings now became a scene of fearful congestion.

What happens when two hundred cars an hour come pouring down the river road to the dock and the good old ferryboat, probably named the *DeWitt Clinton* and built in 1870, can carry only fifty cars at a time on a trip that takes forty minutes? The answer, of course, is that some are left behind, and on national holidays, like the Fourth of July and Labor Day, even though the ferry ran all night many harassed motorists had to wait from evening till morning.

From then on this lordly river, whose scenic beauties have been compared to the Rhine, became a formidable obstacle to automobile traffic. Some means had to be found to carry the roads across to the opposite bank. Once it became clear that motorists were willing to pay a toll equal to or greater than the cost of the ferry trip, plans were made for the first vehicular bridge across the lower Hudson. With the blessing of the state in the form of a charter, private capital financed this first project, and in 1924 a high suspension bridge was completed from Anthony's Nose on the east bank to the side of Bear Mountain on the west. This time there were no complaints in the state capital from those interested in the water-born traffic of the river, for the 1600-foot span of the bridge hangs more than 150 feet above high tide. There was a time almost a century and a half earlier, during the Revolution, when every effort was made to block the river right at the point where the bridge now stands. It was here that the mighty double chain, floating on logs, was strung across the water in order to keep the British fleet from plundering the river towns upstream.

Bridges affect the communities that they join together in many unpredictable ways, but if one can believe the local inhabitants the Bear Mountain Bridge holds the record for unforeseen results. Even those working for the Wildlife Conservation Bureau of the State of New York admit that it could have happened. This bridge, as it turned out, carried not only the first cars and trucks over the waters of the Hudson by day, but also the first migration of American opossums by night. This opossum traffic was one-way—to the east—and no tolls were collected. These nocturnal marsupials had long been resident in New Jersey and Pennsylvania, but were rarely seen east of the Hudson River. In the last twenty years, by means of the Bear Mountain Bridge they have become prevalent in Westchester, Putnam, and Dutchess Counties, to the annoyance of all chicken farmers.

In the eleven years from 1924 to 1935, despite the depression, the automobile traffic in the valley more than doubled. As a result, during these eleven years three more bridges were built across the Hudson. First came the Mid-Hudson at Poughkeepsie (1930), then the George Washington at Fort Lee (1931), and then the Rip Van Winkle at Catskill (1935). With the completion of this latter bridge there were then four modern bridges spanning the river at approximately thirty-five-mile intervals. The least interesting of these new bridges is the Rip Van Winkle, which is made up of a series of trusses with a medium-length cantilever span over the channel in the river. However, this is a very popular bridge, giving direct access to the Catskill Mountain resorts, and from its open deck one can see the old Mountain House, above Palen Cove, which before the Civil War entertained a brilliant gathering of rich and fashionable sightseers.

The Mid-Hudson River Bridge is generally considered to be the most strikingly handsome suspension bridge across the river. Its lean towers stand 1500 feet apart and are made of cellular-steel construction like those of the Philadelphia-Camden Bridge across the Delaware. In a structure as impersonal as a suspension bridge it seems impossible that the designer can leave his individual imprint. Yet, in comparing these towers with those that support the span across the Delaware (page 74) one can see a marked similarity, and naturally so, for both designs came from the drafting board of Ralph Modjeski, who was one of our leading bridge engineers. This bridge is operated by the New York State Bridge Authority, and there is no better proof of its need and popularity than the fact that in twenty-four years it paid off enough of its initial cost so that the toll charges could be cut in half. At the present rate many of the toll bridges across the Hudson will soon have paid off their debt and may become free bridges for the next generation.

For the first twenty-seven miles of its course northward from the Battery, the middle of the Hudson River is the boundary between New Jersey and New York States. These two states also share the harbor. In 1921, after a hundred years of bitter rivalry, the states signed a port treaty establishing a joint agency known as the Port of New York Authority. This agency has two jobs— to expedite the movement of goods and people through the Port of New York by developing and operating better transportation facilities, and to protect and promote commercial interests within the area. In other words, it is up to the Port Authority to see that the vast industrial region that it serves does not choke itself to death with its own traffic, whether rail, ship, plane, or automobile.

The Authority began its work by tackling the problem of get-

ting more automobiles back and forth across the river between Manhattan and New Jersey. After the First World War the ferry-boats were jammed to capacity, but though they carried twelve million vehicles a year they could not relieve the growing congestion on both shores. At that time, the Holland Tunnel was already under construction. The Authority's first answer to the problem of getting traffic across the Hudson was the opening of this tunnel in 1927; the second answer was the completion of the George Washington Bridge four years later, in 1931. There seemed little reason to doubt that these two great arterial facilities could handle all the traffic for some time. However, in ten years the problem had become more complex and had an element of mystery about it, for by 1935 thirty million vehicles crossed the river. The mystery was that the ferries, instead of going out of business, still carried their annual capacity of twelve million, while at the same time another twelve million went via the tunnel and six million by way of the bridge. No one knew where the extra eighteen million vehicles came from or where they were going, but there they were at the tollgates, and every year thereafter their numbers increased. Traffic engineers refer to this increased number of vehicles as "self-generated" traffic, but though they have given it a name they are unable to predict or control its growth.

During the 1920s, even before the Holland Tunnel was completed, the Port Authority recognized the need for another river crossing at the opposite end of the island near 178th Street. The Authority asked its chief engineer, O. H. Ammann, who in 1914 had helped Lindenthal on the Hell Gate arch, to draw the plans for such a structure. Under his direction one of the greatest modern suspension bridges took form on the drafting tables. His final design was as audacious in engineering conception as it was logical in meeting the requirements of the site chosen for the bridge. The vast space between the two steep banks of the Hudson was to be conquered by a single span more than half a mile in length.

A technical comparison of the dimensions of one bridge with those of another is of little interest except to professional bridge engineers who understand the mathematical calculations that determine these dimensions. However, there are certain general features about the George Washington Bridge that set it apart from all other suspension bridges. This bridge fulfills John Roebling's most optimistic prophecies, and the methods of erecting it were basically the same as those used for the Brooklyn Bridge. However, the four cables—each one mile long and 3 feet in diameter—were spun mechanically, so that the time of erection was cut to a quarter of that taken on the older bridge. On the Jersey side, these massive cables enter narrow sloping tunnels that lead down to the larger anchorage chambers set deep in the hard, basaltic rock of the Palisades. The Manhattan anchorage is a monolithic cube of concrete almost the size of a city block.

A modern bridge designed solely to carry automobiles, trucks, and buses brings up a new and complicated set of problems in the matter of approaches to the bridge itself. As long as the bridge was the extension of only one road, the movement of vehicles onto it, across it, and away from it was simple enough. But the George Washington Bridge connects two densely populated urban areas, already congested with local traffic, and the vehicles using it, instead of coming from one road, converge on it from three or four main arterial highways. This necessitated the laying out of an intricate system of one-way ramps and roadways that offered easy access to the bridge from many directions; and, in reverse order, for travelers leaving the bridge there had to be another maze that would unscramble the traffic, allowing each vehicle to seek its own chosen route. Instead of resembling the usual clover-leaf design that serves well enough in simpler situations, the approaches to this bridge, when seen from the air, look very much like a pile of spaghetti, and woe to the confused motorist who makes a wrong turn, for he may find himself recrossing the bridge before he can find his way out. This nest of intertwining roads that form the approaches to the bridge represents more than one-third of the total cost of the project.

There is one other feature that deserves special mention; that is the towers. As originally designed, these enormous steel pylons were to be faced with a curtain wall of limestone. When the giant legs and cross members had reached their full height of 600 feet above the water, those who came to watch the bridge during its erection were so impressed with the functional beauty of the unadorned towers that a popular demand was made not to encase their open steel construction in masonry. This was indeed a triumph of good sense and good taste. In less than three generations of use, structural steel was now accepted as a building material that was not only utilitarian and economical, but also, when used correctly, handsome and dignified in its own right.

From the day the George Washington Bridge opened it has carried more traffic than originally predicted. During the last few summers, over week-ends, the number of cars on the bridge has reached flood proportions; for five or six hours at a time a hundred and fifty cars a minute line up at the toll booths. No one knows better than the Authority what it means to handle such a peak-hour "rush." When a large number of people decide to move en masse in one direction on wheels, and are determined to get where they are going in the least possible time and all at once—then anything can happen. Simple mishaps like flat tires and empty gas tanks suddenly become major catastrophes that bring the long, whirring lines of traffic to a standstill far above the surface of the river. At one time or another, almost every circumstance that can overtake a human being, including birth and death, has occurred on the bridge. Car thieves have tried to use the hours of congestion to smuggle stolen cars from one state to another; and kidnapers have foolishly chosen the bridge as a means of escape. The sweep of the main span has served as a set for making motion pictures, and the steel towers have formed a background for young ladies modeling women's fashions.

No matter who uses the bridge, or for what purpose, the structure itself seems to stand aloof, to the eyes motionless, unaffected by the thrust and impact of forty thousand tires on its

broad pavements. As night overtakes the late Sunday "rush," the lights on the bridge come on and the sweeping parabolas of the cables are reflected across the Hudson. At the top of the tower on the Manhattan side an airplane beacon light blinks its warning. The supporting cables, 3 feet in diameter, contain over twenty-six thousand separate wires, each one of which helps to bear the main span in its 3500-foot leap from tower to tower. These cables, in passing over the shoulders of the steel-grid towers, rest on huge, movable saddle castings that stand in weatherproof rooms. Seen from these enclosures in the late afterglow of a summer evening, the red and white lights of the cars, creeping like an illuminated centipede hundreds of feet below, seem far away.

In these rooms at the top of the towers there is silence, for not even the traffic noises can reach this height. Unless there is a strong wind, one can place one's hand on the taut strands without feeling the slightest tremor in the cables that rise from the center of the bridge and then plunge down to their anchorages on the other side. But the bridge, in adjusting itself to the constant changes in load, in temperature, and in wind force, can be said to move, though its movement is imperceptible to the eyes. Standing at the very center of the main span one is aware of a steady throbbing vibration caused by the regular flow of passenger cars. This vibration will vary ever so slightly when two or three fifteen-ton trucks pound across at thirty miles an hour. In the case of the George Washington Bridge, even when all lanes are filled to capacity with vehicles bumper-to-bumper, this live load still remains less than ten per cent of the dead-weight load of the bridge itself. In other words, to be strong enough to support itself, the bridge is so heavy that in comparison the weight of two thousand vehicles on its pavements is inconsequential.

After the completion of the Rip Van Winkle Bridge in 1935 it was another twenty years before any new bridges across the

Hudson were undertaken. During World War II, steel went into guns rather than into bridges, and for one year, in 1943, at the height of the gas-rationing period, the tollgates at these bridges rang up less fares than ever before. However, after this brief lapse, the traffic volume again began to rise and the summer week-end "rushes" became heavier each year. To say that those responsible for long-range traffic planning have always underestimated the future increase in privately owned automobiles, as well as in trucks and buses, is not to tell the full story. Many city planners and traffic engineers have seen what was coming but could do little about it until the over-all demand for better roads and better bridges became an irrepressible political issue in the state legislatures. In Albany a long-range plan for additional bridges across the Hudson had been developed during those twenty years when there was no bridgebuilding. This plan included a bridge between Rhinecliff and Kingston, as well as another crossing north of the Rip Van Winkle Bridge, midway to Albany. The placing of the New York State Thruway Bridge at one of the widest parts of the Hudson, known as the Tappan Zee, at Nyack, was an afterthought, and its final location was determined almost entirely by the alignment or route that the Thruway would follow as it headed south toward New York City.

None of these new bridges will be long-span suspension bridges. For the most part, their designs have been dictated by the sites chosen for the bridges as well as for economic reasons. The Thruway Bridge, which was completed in 1955, is an extended causeway for more than half of the crossing. This causeway rises slowly to a long cantilever bridge that carries the pavement high above the ship channel. The substructure that supports this bridge is of a special design. Instead of the usual caissons for the founding of the piers, huge cement boxes, built in dry docks nearby, were floated into position before being sunk into the mud of the river's bottom. In one sense these boxes act somewhat like pontoons, in that they have a degree of bouyancy which offsets the downward thrust of the dead weight of the bridge. The width of the river at this point ruled out the possibility of a suspension bridge.

The Kingston Bridge, designed by Doctor David Steinman, should be completed by 1957. The location of this bridge was determined after a long and careful traffic study. Authorities changed the bridge site to a place three miles upstream from the old ferry crossing in order to keep the approaches away from already congested areas. Again, this location was not suitable for a long-span suspension bridge, but, to judge from the design, the ten lofty, 800-foot spans striding across the river should make this a very handsome bridge. These spans will be the second-largest truss spans in the world and will carry a 36-foot open deck above them. Here at last will be a bridge that will allow those using it to see the surrounding country. Nothing is more disappointing than to find oneself poised high above a river with a commanding view of the valley and then to be shut in by a grid of steel girders that block out the landscape. From the deck of this new bridge, going westward, one should have a magnificent, unobstructed view of the whole range of the Catskill Mountains.

The last bridge to be constructed will be somewhere between Albany and Hudson, and its exact position will depend on where the Berkshire Thruway strikes the river.

Looking over the history of the Hudson River Valley one is struck by the part that the river has played, first as a great artery of traffic, and second as a physical barrier for those living on opposite banks. The Dutch, the English, and the Palatinate Germans settled indiscriminately on both sides, but their destinies were not the same. The great estates and plantations of the Beekmans, Van Rensselaers, and Livingstons gave the east shore a prosperity and an aristocratic tradition unknown on the west side, which for years remained sparsely settled by small landowners. But this was the old matter of "the right side and the wrong side of the tracks" on a larger scale, and it is doubtful whether bridges built a hundred years earlier would have changed it.

However, with the coming of the automobile age and the existing bridges, these local differences are disappearing along with the rural character of the countryside. When studying the directional movement of traffic, traffic engineers plot on a map what are known as "destination lines," which indicate not only where automobiles come from and where they are going but also how many take that route, and how often they use it. The "destination lines" in the Hudson Valley are no longer just up and down its length, but also across it. These new habits of travel by millions of motorists will more than justify the building of seven bridges across the Hudson in thirty-five years, or what amounts to one new bridge every five years.

motor vehicles in this country had reached twenty million. Unfortunately these millions were not evenly distributed across the country, but were concentrated in the densely populated centers. There they immediately found themselves in competition with horse-drawn vehicles, with electric trolleys, and with one another for places on the already congested thoroughfares. The older, more compact cities of the East, such as Boston, New York, and Philadelphia, were the first to feel the pressure of their presence in great numbers; but almost simultaneously, despite the wide-open spaces between, San Francisco began to suffer the same self-strangulation. Massed on the tip of a peninsula, jammed between the hills and the harbor, the crowded streets of this picturesque city offered scant accommodations for the ever-increasing number of new automobiles.

The shape of San Francisco Bay has been likened to a frisky whale whose tail points to the south and whose waterspout follows the course of the San Joaquin River. Today this vast bay area, almost 160 miles in length, has a population of three million and includes more than seventy separate communities. Despite the fact that the only land approach to San Francisco is from the south, across rough mountain country, the Bay area has remained during its brief but exciting hundred years of existence

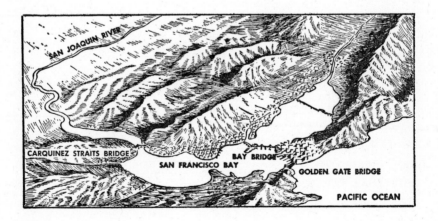

the heart and brain of this great harbor settlement. Once the boom-or-bust days of the gold rush were over, this magnificent natural harbor quickly grew into the largest industrial seaport on the Pacific coast. Until the various bridges in the Bay area were built, the city's huge sprawling complex of homes and factories, railway terminals and wharfs, shipyards and farms, was held together by an efficient fleet of fast, hard-working ferryboats. In 1930 this ferry system was handling four million vehicles and fifty million passengers a year. By any standard this was a heroic job of water-borne transportation, but the demand for a bridge across the Golden Gate and one across the Bay remained as insistent as ever, and by 1937 both bridges had been completed.

It is in keeping with the scale and grandeur of San Francisco Bay that its two bridges should set world records, one being the largest and the other having the longest span. The San Francisco–Oakland Bay Bridge has an upper and lower deck; the upper carries passenger cars only, and the lower is for trucks and interurban electric trains. The Golden Gate Bridge has a single deck used entirely for motor transportation. Both bridges are toll bridges, and were financed as self-liquidating public facilities. In the last few years the Bay Bridge has been carrying almost twice the number of cars that use the Golden Gate, but in each case the bridges have far surpassed their estimated traffic volumes, and the week-end "rushes" on these bridges are comparable to those on the George Washington.

The complete story of the design and construction of these bridges would make a book in itself. The Bay Bridge has a total length of a little more than eight miles, four and one-quarter of them being over water. From downtown San Francisco going east, one crosses the West Bay to Yerba Buena Island on twin suspension bridges. The island is pierced by a tunnel, through which one reaches the beginning of the East Bay section of the bridge. This is made up of a high cantilever span, 1400 feet long, from which the highway drops down through five truss spans to the long eastern causeway that leads into the city of Oakland. In comparison the Golden Gate Bridge is a simple and classic example of the single, long-span, suspension bridge. Its 750-foot towers carry the structure across three-quarters of a mile of open water where the racing tides of the Pacific sweep in and out of the harbor at seven miles an hour.

These two bridges mark a high point in the art and science of bridgebuilding. Behind them stands the accumulated experience of bridge engineers during the last half-century. This experience has been formulated into a vast body of systematic knowledge which is shared by the profession as a whole. It is this background of factual information that forms the basis for technical advances in bridge engineering, and as a result the design and construction of modern bridges now follow very exact and standardized patterns of procedure. However, when one sets out to build two such structures as the Golden Gate and the Bay Bridges the very immensity of these projects brings up new difficulties and new problems. Special situations arose in the construction of both the substructures and the superstructures on these bridges, and the answers to these difficulties were not to be found within the covers of a book.

One of the most remarkable feats of construction was the founding of the central pier (W 4) on the western section of the Bay Bridge. This pier stands midway between San Francisco and Yerba Buena Island. It is an enormous mass of steel and concrete—literally, a half-submerged skyscraper—that serves as the anchorage for the cables of the twin suspension bridges. At this point in the harbor the rock strata lies 220 feet below the surface. Such depth was too great for men to work in the usual compressed-air caissons, and to complicate matters the tidal currents sweeping the surface of the Bay were very strong. The building of the central pier required a special caisson in the shape of a gigantic box filled with fifty-five steel cylinders, each 15 feet in diameter, sealed at the top with a watertight but removable cover. This caisson resembled one of the old-fashioned multiple molds used for making candles. Fabricated in a dry dock, this vast honeycomb of steel was towed into position, anchored, then slowly sunk into the mud.

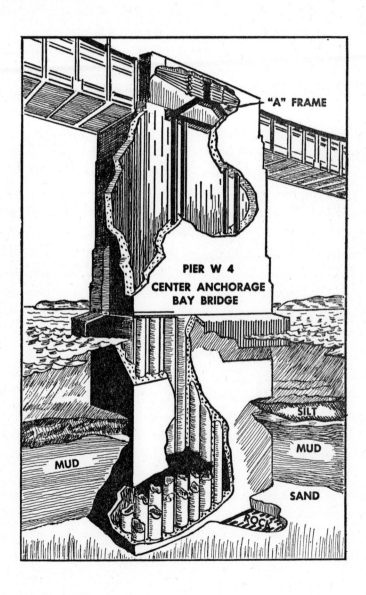

The next operation was to fill the spaces around and between the cylinders with concrete. Once the concrete had set, the tops of the steel cylinders were opened and clamshell buckets were lowered through them to remove the mud below the caisson and permit the caisson to settle slowly to the rock bed. As the cutting edge of the caisson sank, new sections were added to the sides and to the cylinders above water. To set such an artificial mountain firmly and evenly on the rock strata required the help of deep-sea divers who directed operations from the bottom.

The founding of the substructure of the Bay Bridge can be likened to the erection of a forty-story office building, occupying a full city block, more than half of which has to be constructed under water. Only by means of an ingenious system of air ballasting in the capped steel cylinders could such a mammoth structure be lowered evenly through the muck and tides of the Bay. As the drawing (page 101) shows, strands forming the cables are attached to a heavy "A" frame at the top of this anchorage pier. In this way the dead-weight loads (thirty million pounds per cable) are counterbalanced. A variation in the weight of live loads on different sections of the bridge is taken up by the "A" frame which is anchored to the base foundations of pier W 4. This pier sets the record in depth and size for any bridge substructure ever undertaken.

The southern pier of the Golden Gate Bridge stands in the open ocean, more than a thousand feet from the shore. In the course of its construction it was rammed by a freighter in the fog and threatened by countless storms. This massive foundation on which the 750-foot tower stands is a pier built within a pier. The outer ring or elliptical fender protects it from the sea as well as from passing ships. The fender, 300 feet long and 155 feet wide, rests on bedrock 100 feet below the water level and was generally referred to by those working on the bridge as the "bathtub," because of its shape. Before the fender was entirely

completed an attempt was made to float a compressed-air caisson inside it, in order to found the interior pier. Despite the
great weight of the caisson, the long swells of the Pacific tossed
it about, and because the fender itself was being endangered,
the caisson was hastily removed. A quick decision was necessary, and the engineers immediately ordered the completion of
the fender. Once the "bathtub" was finished it was filled with
concrete to a depth of 65 feet and then pumped dry. In other
words, the fender became a cofferdam until the interior pier
had been completed.

The legs of the towers on both bridges are of the usual cellular-steel construction; those on the Golden Gate Bridge are
braced horizontally, those on the Bay Bridge diagonally. The
towers on the latter bridge are designed to carry a maximum
load of sixty-five million pounds. Because of the length of the
cables on the Bay Bridge, either a rapid variation in temperature or a concentration of live load on one part of the bridge
is sufficient to cause a slight back-and-forth movement of these

cables. This motion, instead of making the cables slide in their saddles at the top of the towers, causes the tower itself to bend from its true perpendicular position as much as 3 feet in the direction of the greatest pull. Only steel has the strength and elasticity to stand such pressures, for such a movement would rack a masonry tower to pieces in no time.

As we have seen, the stiffening truss of a suspension bridge helps to distribute the weight of the live loads along the length of the bridge, as well as to stabilize it against wind forces. On the Golden Gate Bridge the accepted procedures for erecting this truss were carried out; that is, the truss was built out from the towers in both directions, section by section, each being supported by hangars from the cables above. On the suspension section of the Bay Bridge a new method of erection was used. The stiffening truss on this bridge is particularly heavy, having been designed to carry a two-level roadway.

The steel members for each section of this truss were first assembled on shore; then the whole section was lifted onto a barge and towed out to the bridge site. A form of lifting apparatus that looked very much like an overhead crane was slung between the two main cables. The electric hoisting engines were mounted on the piers at the base of the towers. As is shown in the drawing opposite, the four sets of hoisting cables ran from these engines to the top of the towers, from there to the lifting strut between the suspension cables, and then down to the new section waiting on the barge below. After a little experience, and by means of a careful control system, the operators were able to pick up a section from the barge and, holding it level during the lifting operation, raise it to its final position in ten minutes. However, the time saved by this new method of erection was not as great as had been hoped, for the tidal currents in the Bay hampered the towing and anchoring of the barges.

The San Francisco–Oakland Bay Bridge was completed in 1936 and the Golden Gate Bridge a year later. There is no ques-

tion that the Golden Gate Bridge is one of the most beautiful
modern bridges in the world. This is due not only to its enormous span length, which in all probability will be exceeded in
the next ten years, but more especially to the magnificent location of the bridge and the superb way in which it meets the
challenge of this site. The lean strength and simplicity of the
tapering, set-back towers, the seeming delicacy of the long main
span, and the way in which the massive cables appear to be
anchored at one end by a city and at the other by a mountain
range—all combine to make the Golden Gate a contemporary

Colossus, not of Rhodes, but of our own great technological civilization.

Many argue that the Bay Bridge is not one bridge but a series of bridges linked by a large tunnel. In any event this eight-mile engineering project carries one of the heaviest loads of traffic in the country, and since World War II its annual traffic count has far exceeded its designed capacity. This does not mean that the weight of live loads on this bridge is too great for it to bear, but, as on the George Washington, traffic during the rush-hour jams has reached the saturation point. For the last eight years the increase has been at the rate of one million cars a year, and the latest records show that fifty-five million cars now cross the bridge every year.

It was perfectly evident ten years ago that more bridges would be needed in the San Francisco Bay area, and the greatest demand was for another bridge between San Francisco and Oakland. The first and simplest answer to this problem caught the popular fancy; that was to build a second Bay bridge, identical in every way, that would parallel the existing one.

Each bridge would be one-way and, though this might be an expensive solution, it would certainly relieve the situation for a long time to come. The idea of building parallel bridges was not a new one. Years before, a parallel bridge across the Mississippi at St. Louis had been built next to the old Eads Bridge. However, this time traffic engineers and city planners pointed out that a double bridge across the bay would only double traffic congestion at the bridge approaches both in San Francisco and Oakland. These experts saw that the problem was to disperse traffic rather than let it stagnate at the ends of a double bridge. Their recommendation was to remove the interurban railway tracks from the existing bridge, widen the upper roadway, and then build a second crossing farther south that would connect the city proper with Alameda. This scheme was known as the "Southern Crossing."

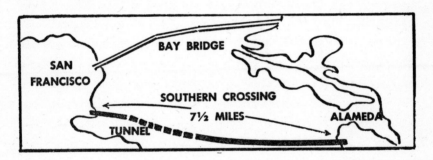

For eight years the case of the southern crossing was debated in the California state legislature. While the automobiles on the Bay Bridge increased by millions, the reports and counter-reports on this alternate scheme also grew until they filled many fat volumes. Only recently has the issue been settled; the construction of a southern crossing, as indicated on the map, will begin in 1956. There have been many strange bridges built in this country, but the plans for this project are unique, and the term "crossing" describes it far better than "bridge." Starting from San Francisco, the motorist will drive east across the Bay for one mile on a low trestle or six-lane viaduct. This will lead him to a man-made sand island where he will plunge into one of three two-lane tubes that will carry him deep beneath the ship channel. He will then emerge at a second artificial island and continue for four miles across the bay on a low causeway to the opposite shore.

This is indeed an unusual way to extend a road across, or more accurately under, a natural obstacle. Among the many engineering considerations were those brought forward by the Navy. From the standpoint of national defense bridges are necessary, but today they are vulnerable to air attack. A bombed bridge might well block that part of the harbor for months, whereas a flooded tube would not interfere with naval ship movements. This point was considered when the Golden Gate Bridge was first proposed, but at the entrance to the Bay the water is so deep that should the main span of the Golden Gate fall it would sink far below the keels of the largest ships.

At present another bridge is being built across San Francisco Bay between Richmond and San Raphael. When this double-deck cantilever bridge and the southern crossing are complete, the Bay area will be laced across by six vehicular and two railway bridges. What is now taking place in this great western harbor is very similar to the situation in the New York–New Jersey metropolitan area. As we trace the pattern of growth in these two vital seaports, we see that the same things happened and that the same forces have been at work. The tendency of shipping is to concentrate all terminal facilities into one area like filings grouped about a magnet. On the other hand, the privately owned automobile and the truck can move in any direction and make it possible for people to spread out into other communities, thus creating a new pattern of growth that tends toward decentralization. Shipping built the harbor cities, automobiles the suburbs, and only bridges and tunnels can hold them together.

VIII. No Two Bridges Are Alike

THOUGH most of today's bridges are built to serve the motorist, he of all people gets the least chance really to see them. If the bridge stands in flat country, its silhouette may rise above the horizon, but the distant view is limited, for in most cases the roads heading toward it run in the same direction as the axis of the bridge. As the motorist glides up the long approaches of a suspension bridge, he may get some idea of the scale and majesty of the supporting towers, or, in the fleeting moment that he crosses the main span, can notice the graceful arc of the cables above, but rarely if ever does he see the bridge as a whole.

Perhaps it is this difficulty that accounts for an habitual indifference toward the structure that supports them on the part of those who have seen it only from the driver's seat. Maybe the true student of bridges should always go by boat. There is no question that one can get a better idea of the great spans that cross the Hudson River from the deck of the Albany day boat than by days spent motoring up and down that valley. For these same reasons, perhaps few motorists realize the number and variety of bridges that are in daily use throughout the country.

Every year hundreds if not thousands of new bridges are being built. The great majority of these are short-span over- or underpass bridges used on express highways. Judged as bridge structures, they may not be very impressive in size and shape, but our modern "thruways" are utterly dependent on them, and without them, no matter how many lanes were provided, traffic would move as slowly as on a village main street. The New Jersey Turnpike often handles sixty to seventy thousand cars a day. If it were not for the many over- or underpass bridges, all local traffic within the region would remain as completely cut off and isolated on its own side as though a mighty river in full flood bisected the state. Reliance on one grade crossing with a traffic light would immediately create a vast, stagnant lake of motorcars. In order to maintain an even flow of traffic at sixty miles per hour along its 118 miles, the New Jersey Turnpike was forced to construct five major bridges and some two hundred and sixty other structures which average out at somewhat more than two crossings a mile.

So far in this book the more spectacular bridges in America

have been dealt with. As already explained, these bridges come under three conventional classifications—the steel-arch, the cantilever, and the suspension bridge. Their great size and the length of their soaring spans set them apart from all other bridges. But one must never forget that no matter how bold the conception or how original the design or construction, these outstanding bridges, like all good engineering projects, are the result of realistic economic considerations.

It is these same economic considerations that have brought into being certain other kinds of bridges that play an important part in the over-all picture of bridges in this country. Today's bridges are all custom-built; no two are identical, for each is designed to meet the special needs of a particular situation. Besides the three conventional types there are movable bridges, like the bascule and vertical-lift bridges; there are bridges that combine causeways, trusses, and cantilever designs in one long structure; and—believe it or not—there is one floating bridge.

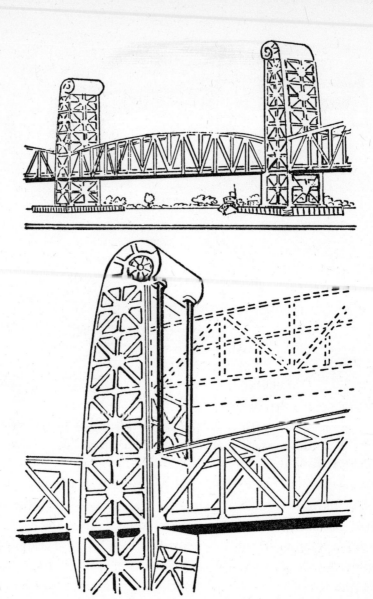

This vertical-lift bridge crosses Rockaway Inlet on the south shore of Long Island. The 540-foot central truss span can be lifted to the height of the towers. Bridges of this kind are operated electrically and are usually used where a wide opening is needed for water-borne traffic. One of the longest lift bridges in the country crosses the Cape Cod Canal.

The movable bridge shown above is known as a double-leaf
"bascule" bridge. Bascule means a weighted lever; the counterbalance weights on this bridge can be seen when it is open or
raised. As the name suggests, this form of drawbridge is very
old and was used to cross the moats surrounding medieval cas-
tles. Electrically operated bascule bridges have taken the place
of the old-fashioned steam-turned swing bridges used by the
railroads. Swing bridges require a central pier usually in the
deepest part of the ship channel, which not only is costly but
also cuts down the size of the opening. Most of the bridges that
cross the canal in Chicago are bascule bridges.

The bridge that crosses the Cooper River near Charleston, South Carolina, is unique. Made up of two cantilevers, a number of long open-deck truss spans, and a connecting causeway, it is an excellent example of what might be called a combination bridge. This is a relatively narrow bridge and its great height and steep approaches give it a roller-coaster appearance; the fact that the sky-flown roadway curves recklessly at the center of the bridge adds to this impression

Most floating bridges are temporary military structures, and after serving to get an army across they are usually destroyed.

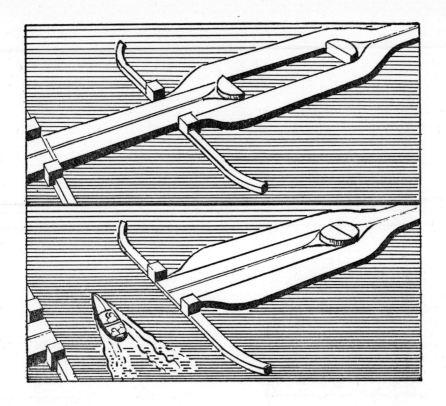

However, the one that crosses Lake Washington near Seattle is a permanent floating bridge. For a mile and a quarter of its total length, this bridge is supported by hollow, concrete box-pontoons which are anchored in shallow water above a sunken island. The bridge is held in a stable position through a system of tensioned cables. The water-borne traffic on the lake is mostly pleasure boats, and one section of the bridge (shown above) telescopes into a kind of wharf, thus affording a 200-foot opening so that boats can pass from one side of the lake to the other. The Lake Washington Floating Bridge was not built as a stunt. It is a practical engineering solution for a particular situation, and its success was proved during the first year after its completion in 1940 when one and a half million vehicles crossed it.

IX. Tomorrow's Suspension Bridges

AS ABRAM HEWITT, Congressman from New York,
stated at the opening of the Brooklyn Bridge, the bridge
engineer's basic concern is to produce absolute stability out of
unstable elements or "confess inglorious failure." Whether or
not the modern bridgebuilder can always achieve absolute stability may be open to question, but his record in terms of bridge
failures has been remarkably good. In the last half-century there
have been only two major disasters on long-span bridges, the
first being the collapse of the Quebec cantilever bridge during
its construction (see page 64), and the second the destruction
of the deck of the Tacoma Narrows Bridge in a wind storm in
1940.

These two famous bridge failures have many factors in common. Neither was the result of negligence, and in each case the
destruction was caused by forces that were beyond the calculation of engineers at the time. They were similar also in that, as
a result of the investigations that followed each of them, there
was a critical reappraisal of the current theories of long-span
bridge design, as well as of the techniques of construction. The
George Washington Bridge proved once and for all the great
tensile strength of the supporting steel cables, and from there
on, suspension-bridge designers felt justified in building lighter
structures that were still capable of carrying their own dead
weights as well as the comparatively light vehicular live loads
for which they were designed. In a few years' time this new
trend in suspension-bridge design resulted in the building of a
number of graceful structures such as the Deer Island Bridge
in Maine, the Bronx–Whitestone Bridge in New York, and the
Tacoma Bridge that crosses Lake Washington near Seattle.

The Tacoma Bridge, when completed, was the third longest in
the country, but was also, in relation to the length of its main
span, the narrowest suspension bridge ever built. The bridge's
slim proportions in no way affected its ability to support itself
or its loads, but it soon gave evidence of being an extremely
flexible structure. Even in gentle breezes its undulating movements won it the nickname of "Galloping Gertie."

Four months after completion, in November 1940, the deck
of the Tacoma Bridge was ripped apart in a wind storm and
collapsed. Unlike the sudden cataclysm of buckling steel that
wrecked the Quebec Bridge, the Tacoma suspension bridge
went through four hours of convulsive gyrations before it fell to
pieces. Fortunately there is an accurate motion-picture record
of the bridge's struggle to maintain its stability during this long
ordeal. At seven o'clock in the morning the wind was blowing
at forty-two miles per hour and the main span of the bridge was
heaving up and down with a slow waving motion much like a
pennant flapping in the breeze. By ten o'clock the waves passing along the length of the bridge were almost 30 feet high from
trough to crest. Then without warning, and with no change in
wind velocity, a new rhythm set in that caused the deck to
twist in a kind of corkscrew undulation. A half-hour later the
first breakage occurred when a floor panel at midspan broke
away and fell into the water. A few minutes later a number of
hangers that connected the deck to the cables snapped, and
600 feet of the main span somersaulted into Lake Washington.
For a few moments the writhing convulsions ceased and the
bridge appeared to steady itself. But soon a new series of
tremors began and as these increased into wild, rhythmic movements the whole of the main span tore loose. Without the
counterbalancing weight of the deck, the two 1000-foot side
spans first rose into the air and then sagged down, thus com-
pleting the wreck.

The Tacoma Bridge had been built to stand any static wind

pressures caused by gales up to one hundred twenty miles per hour. Why then had the bridge disintegrated in a wind that was only one-third that force? The towers and supporting cables of the bridge remained unaffected. What was it that had changed the natural swaying motion of a suspended structure into a series of vast, racking contortions that finally tore ten thousand tons of steel to shreds? As one might have guessed, the answer to these questions could be found only in the new science of aerodynamics. The highly specialized knowledge that had made it possible for us to overcome "wing flutter" in airplanes was now used to analyze the aerodynamic effect of wind on suspension bridges.

One of the outstanding figures in the investigation of this problem has been Doctor David B. Steinman, who for the last fifteen years has made an exhaustive study of model bridges in wind tunnels. Like many other bridge engineers, Doctor Stein-man recognized that this was no new problem, and that in the light of current knowledge it would appear that the failure of Colonel Ellett's Wheeling bridge, across the Ohio, was caused by the same aerodynamic forces. There are a number of pro-posed solutions to this problem that go beyond John Roebling's original answer, which, as you may remember, was based on the use of a heavy stiffening truss and wind stays. When completed, the Bronx–Whitestone Bridge showed the same tendency as the Tacoma toward extreme flexibility. As a result of the further investigation of wind forces on suspension bridges, a series of diagonal hangers between the cables and the deck was added, thus forming a very rigid truss. Other preventive measures that have been recommended include the streamlining of the steel shapes of bridge members, along with a system of air vents in the deck for free wind passage.

During the twenty years before the failure of the Tacoma Bridge, this country erected at least a dozen of the finest long-span suspension bridges ever built. All are in constant use today and all are indispensable in our present system of land trans-portation. Whether judged from an economic standpoint as self-liquidating public facilities, or considered solely as great land-marks in the age-old tradition of bridgebuilding, they are com-pletely successful. It was the Second World War and not the Tacoma Bridge disaster that brought an end to this particular period of bridge construction. That it took a hundred years to recognize and correctly diagnose the aerodynamic effects of wind on suspension bridges is understandable, but it would now appear that these forces can be controlled.

With this last problem behind us, what then of the new bridges that are on the drafting boards today? Our contempo-rary bridge engineers have stepped up Roebling's prophecy. They now set a limit of 10,000 feet for the main spans of tomor-row's suspension bridges. Will they ever reach it?

One of the larger suspension bridges now under construction will cross the Mackinac Straits that connect Lake Huron and Lake Michigan. Doctor Steinman is the consulting engineer on the new project, which, when completed in 1957, will fulfill a seventy-year dream of a direct connection between Michigan's upper and lower peninsulas. Though the 3800-foot main span is only 300 feet greater than that of the George Washington, the bridge's total suspended length of more than a mile and a half

between the cable anchorages will make it the longest suspended structure built thus far. As the drawing (page 121) indicates, the design calls for a deep, heavy stiffening truss that lies below the deck.

As is so often the case with bridges, that part which cannot be seen—the substructure—is the most interesting feature from an engineering point of view. At the bridge site the bedrock lies slightly more than 200 feet beneath the surface of the Straits, and here it was necessary to use caissons somewhat similar to those employed on the Bay Bridge at San Francisco. However, here the concrete was not mixed before being poured into the bottom of the caissons; instead, the crushed stone alone was first dumped into place and then, by means of flexible pipes, the cement and sand were pumped under high pressure into every opening between the stones, thus consolidating them into a solid concrete mass. The method of intruding cement under water has proved very economical in the building of deep substructures.

Though in this book we are primarily concerned with bridges in the United States, it seems entirely justifiable to call attention to the proposed Messina Straits Bridge in Italy (shown opposite). Its designer, Doctor Steinman, is an American, and, as the drawing indicates, this huge suspension bridge will incorporate his latest methods of wind bracing to overcome the effects of aerodynamic forces. In order to leap from the toe of the boot of Italy to the island of Sicily the bridge will require a main span of 5000 feet. Such a bridge will have to withstand not only the gales that sweep this part of the Mediterranean, but also earthquakes. Not least of the engineering hazards will be the placing of foundations at a depth of 400 feet in swirling tides of the Straits. The erection of a bridge at this site will doubtless put the science of modern bridgebuilding to its greatest test. Can our engineering skill overcome the ancient, legendary terrors of Scylla and Charybdis?

The Port of New York Authority also has its own terrors to deal with, though they are not legendary. The recurrent nightmare for the Authority is the vision of eight lanes of automobiles, trucks, and buses, standing bumper to bumper, stretching from horizon to horizon, with all their horns blaring in a gigantic wail of frustration. The Authority estimates that the cross-Hudson traffic within the metropolitan area will increase by thirty per cent in the next five years. Also, when one remembers that traffic loads within this area have doubled in the last ten years and that "as a result, the demands on our principal arterial highways, bridges and tunnels have far outstripped their capacities," one can understand the dangers that the Authority foresees. The over-all plan for meeting these conditions does not concern us here. However, there are two proposals of new arterial facilities in the Authority's plan that have a direct bearing on the future of bridges. These are the addition of a lower deck on the George Washington Bridge and the erection of a suspension bridge, across the Upper New York Bay at the Narrows, which will connect Staten Island and Brooklyn.

The original design for the George Washington Bridge called for two decks, but the lower one for trucks and interurban

trains has not been built. The addition of the proposed lower deck will take about two and a half years to complete. At present the bridge is handling 33 million vehicles annually, and the most conservative estimates set a figure of 56 million in ten years' time. With only a few minor changes at the anchorages, the present towers and supporting cables are quite capable of carrying this extra load. In this case the major engineering problem is the design and construction of the additional approaches that will be needed to handle 56 million vehicles. These approaches are the most costly part of the project, particularly those on the New Jersey side, which will have to be cut through the solid rock of the Palisades.

Only a very tired, bored traveler could enter the Port of New York without experiencing a sense of wonder and expectancy. The startling and magnificent view of the waters surrounding Manhattan, as seen from the deck of a liner passing through the Narrows into the Upper Bay, always calls forth some emotional response, whether seen for the first time by a newcomer or for the twentieth by a veteran globe-trotter. In ten years' time or less, the old familiar landmarks such as the Statue of Liberty, the skyline of the city, and that most venerable of structures, the Brooklyn Bridge, will be seen within the frame of the giant towers and the 4400-foot span of the new Narrows Bridge. When this bridge is completed, the two world harbors of our continent—New York and San Francisco—will both be crowned with suspension bridges, breathtaking in the beauty and grandeur of their proportions.

The Narrows Bridge has been designed by O. H. Ammann, the consulting engineer for the Port Authority. It will have two decks, each wide enough for six lanes of traffic. Though the upper deck may not be used at the start, both will be completed when the bridge is opened. One reason for this is to assure wind stability on the long main span by means of a strong stiffening truss. The sections of this truss are novel in design, being constructed on a rigid boxlike frame. The diameter of the cables (36 inches) and the width between them (102 feet) are almost identical with those of the cables on the George Washington Bridge. Though the feet of the towers will rest at the edge of Fort Hamilton, on the east, and of Fort Wadsworth, on the west, the substructure will still have to be founded at 185 feet below the surface of the harbor.

The Narrows Bridge forms an important link in the new plan for traffic arteries that will bypass New York City proper. For years it was taken for granted that those living within the greater metropolitan area had to get to and from Manhattan daily. As the growing suburban centers on the periphery of the New York–New Jersey area become more and more self-sustaining communities, it becomes evident that arterial highways between these communities are needed and that these highways should not be funneled through the already congested approaches to midtown Manhattan. Also, the Narrows Bridge will make it possible for through traffic between the Middle Atlantic states and New England to flow around the metropolitan area. As an arterial facility the new bridge will serve automotive traffic much in the same way that the

Hudson tunnels and the Hell Gate arch serve the railroads.

The immediate future appears to hold little possibility of any new or radical change in the technology of modern bridge construction. Certainly there is nothing to compare with what happened during the last century, when structural steel was first introduced as a bridgebuilding material. The use of pre-stressed concrete may prove more economically feasible; welding, rather than riveting, of bridge structures may increase; and experimentation with light strong metals like aluminum and magnesium will continue; but it is doubtful that any of these will alter the basic designs of long-span bridges as we know them today. In relation to atomic weapons the tunnel offers little more security than the suspension bridge, and it takes many tunnels to handle the same amount of traffic as one bridge.

By the very nature of his profession the bridge engineer must be a perfectionist. In his constant struggle with the forces of nature and in his unending attempt to control the behavior of inanimate materials there is no room for failure. Unlike the theoretical scientist, the engineer's possibilities for experimentation are severely limited for practical reasons.

Lately we have been forced to recognize that our highly complex civilization has a tendency to make specialists of those working in the technical professions. However, the bridge-builder stands apart and above this trend. When called in as consultant on a great public project, he has to be more than merely an expert trained in one compartment of our vast technological knowledge. The bridge designer must be capable of bringing into order the skills and techniques of many varied and highly specialized fields. But beyond this, his approach to the problems of building permanent and beautiful structures must be general, his considerations almost universal.

on to say in his dedication speech at the opening of the Brooklyn Bridge, "Now, turn to the Bridge. It looks like a motionless mass of masonry and metal; but, as a matter of fact, it is instinct with motion. There is not a particle of matter in it which is at rest for the minutest portion of time. It is an aggregation of unstable elements, changing with every change in the temperature, and every movement of the heavenly bodies. The problem was, out of these unstable elements, to produce absolute stability; and it was this problem which the engineers, the organized intelligence, had to solve, or confess to inglorious failure. The problem has been solved."

For most of us the words "stress" and "strain" mean pretty much the same thing, but engineers make a distinction between them. In a bridge structure the over-all pull of gravity produces a series of forces that act upon all the parts or members that go to make up the bridge. Engineers measure the effects of these forces in terms of stresses and strains. Stress is a unit of measurement which relates the amount of force in pounds to the size, or number of square inches of the member on which it is acting. In bridges particularly, this action (stress) produces a change in the length of the member which in turn deforms or alters the shape of the bridge. This change of shape or deformation is measured in units of strain. If a bridge is overloaded or sufficiently stressed we will see every shape within it change as it collapses. On the other hand, we cannot see with the naked eye the strains that are always present in all the members of a self-supporting structure. In a bridge there are two major kinds of stress, one that acts to shorten a member, which is compression, and one that pulls it apart or lengthens it, which is tension.

The attempt in this chapter is to explain the way in which the various bridgebuilding materials withstand or resist these stresses. As you will see, the very natures of these materials have dictated the form that the bridge will take.

Strain is the change of shape accompanying stress.

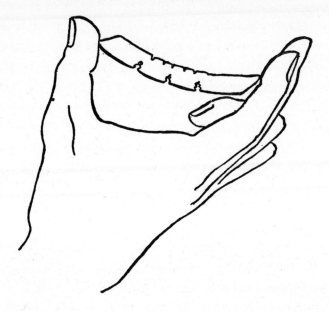

The upper side of the rubber eraser is under compression, and, as it is shortened, wrinkles will appear. The lower side is under tension, and, as it is lengthened, fissures or cracks will appear.

In this case the eraser is bent by the pressure of the thumb and forefinger into the shape of an arc, and stress is produced. In a bridge the stress is caused by the pull of gravity; the amount of stress is determined by the total weight of the bridge plus its load. Solid lines indicate parts under compression. Broken lines indicate parts under tension.

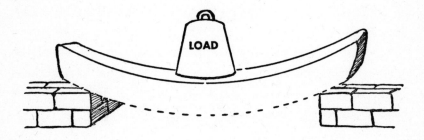

STONE 1

A hard stone such as granite can withstand an enormous compressive force before disintegrating, or changing shape.

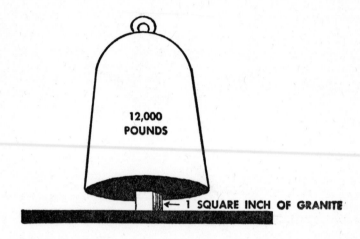

12,000 POUNDS

← 1 SQUARE INCH OF GRANITE

However, in tension this same square inch of stone will break apart under one-tenth the strain.

In fact, a long beam of stone, if unsupported, will crack under its own weight.

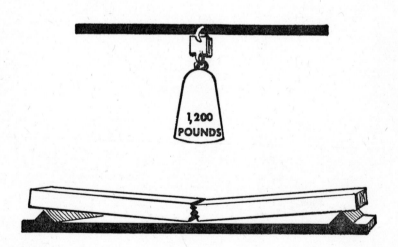

1,200 POUNDS

STONE 2

This type of primitive bridge made of solid stone slabs is known as a "clapper" bridge.

Because of the low tensile strength of stone, these bridges had very narrow spans.

Between the time of the "clapper" bridges and the perfection of the stone arch, awkward forms like these may have been used. Set up in this fashion, these stones are self-supporting, with little or no tension. Only recently, by means of man-made masonry, could such stone shapes be used with economy (see reinforced concrete, page 150).

S T O N E 3

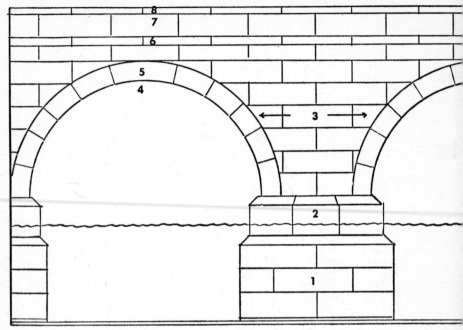

1. Foundation or substructure stands below the water line
2. Piers rest on foundation stones
3. Spandrel or space between arches
4. Crown of the arch or top of the arch
5. Keystone, which holds all the other stones in the arch in place
6. Bottom coping—a projecting line of stones that marks the level of the roadway
7. Parapet or guard rail
8. Top coping that finishes or protects the parapet

In relation to the massive dead-weight load carried by each pier, the live load as represented by teams and wagons would be inconsequential. The semicircular stone arch, as used by the

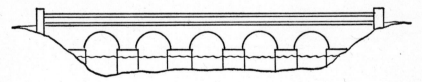

STONE 3

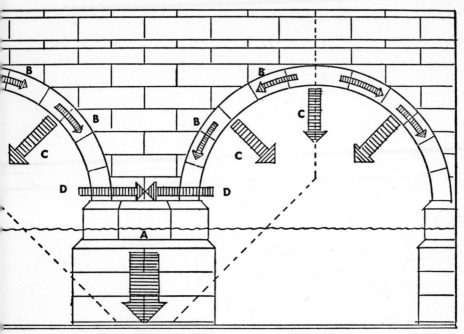

A. The part from the crown of one arch to the crown of the next can be considered as one section of the bridge. The total weight of each of the sections is carried by the pier below it.
B. These arrows indicate the locking action, due to compression, of the curved stones that form the arch.
C. These arrows indicate the wedging action not only of the key-stone but of all the stones in the arch.
D. There is a sidewise thrust at the point where the arch meets the pier. This is counterbalanced arch by arch until the last arch rests on the abutment.

Romans, blocked one-half to two-thirds of the river.

An eighteenth-century bridge like Peronnet's (page 38) took up only one-fifth of the river space.

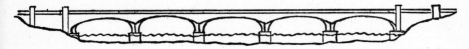

WOOD 1

As a bridgebuilding material, wood is strong in relation to its weight. Under stress, the kind of wood and the particular way in which the grain runs generally determine the limits of its strength. Because wood bends and splits easily, its tensile strength is unreliable.

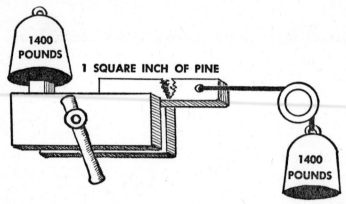

This diagram attempts to show the maximum number of pounds that one square inch of wood (pine) will resist before it changes shape. This figure measures its *ultimate* strength. In practice engineers do not base their calculations on the ultimate strength of the materials they are using. Instead they use a lower figure, known as the working strength. This figure takes into account the inaccuracies of measurement, mistakes in workmanship, and lack of uniformity, which in this case is grain. In other words, the working strength sets up a margin of safety, which varies with each material.

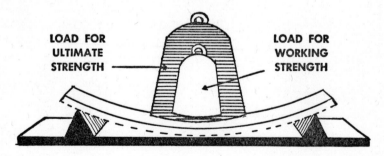

WOOD 2

When a plank's width is doubled, its carrying capacity is doubled.

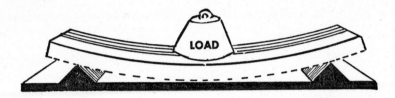

When the same plank's height is doubled, its carrying capacity is quadrupled.

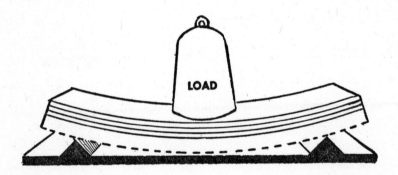

The beam and lintel is the oldest form of wooden structure.

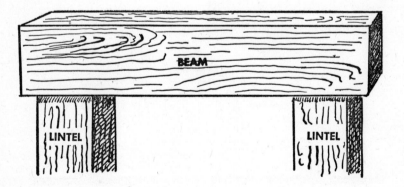

WOOD 3

It is easy to change the shape of a rectangular frame if the joints are held with a single nail. However, when a diagonal is placed across the frame its shape becomes rigid; it now forms two triangles. A triangle is the simplest figure whose shape cannot be altered without changing the length of one or more of its sides.

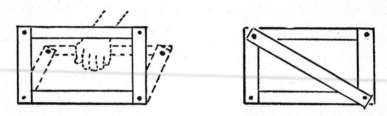

The "king post" is one of the commonest designs used for self-supporting wooden structures. Here the principle of the triangle gives the bridge rigidity.

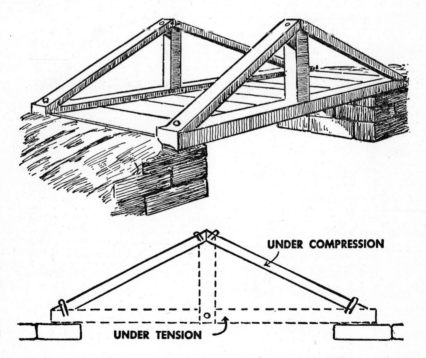

WOOD 4

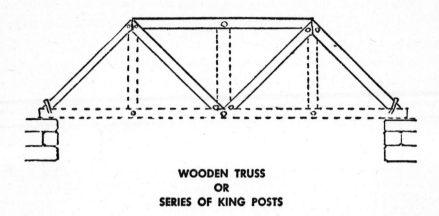

**WOODEN TRUSS
OR
SERIES OF KING POSTS**

If one took a section from a giant Sequoia and cut holes in it, as shown here, it would no longer be a *beam*, but a *truss*. In other words, a truss can be considered as a beam with all unnecessary weight removed.

IRON 1

The ultimate strength of iron is roughly four times greater than stone and thirty times that of wood. Cast iron and wrought iron have the same ability to withstand very high compressive stresses. As a bridgebuilding material, cast iron has proved unreliable when under tension.

Wrought iron has twice to four times the tensile strength of cast iron, depending on how it is processed.

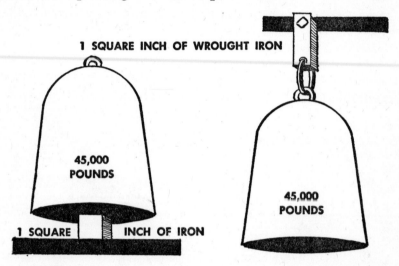

1 SQUARE INCH OF WROUGHT IRON

45,000 POUNDS

1 SQUARE INCH OF IRON

45,000 POUNDS

In 1850 Squire Whipple used both cast iron and wrought iron in his arch truss bridge (see page 40). The bow string or upper chord of his bridge was made of cast iron and was always under compression. All the other members of the bridge were of wrought iron so that they could withstand both compression and tension as moving loads crossed the bridge.

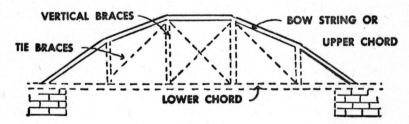

VERTICAL BRACES

TIE BRACES

BOW STRING OR UPPER CHORD

LOWER CHORD

IRON 2

Without any load, the structural members of an iron truss bridge, in supporting the bridge itself, are either under compression (——) or tension (– – –) as shown here.

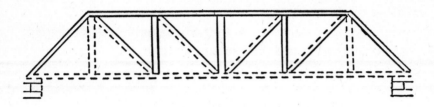

As a heavy load moves across the bridge the position of the structural members is changed moment by moment.

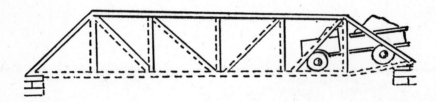

The largest deflection in the top and bottom chords occurs as the load crosses the center of the span. As long as the load is moving across the bridge there is a constant change of stress in the vertical and diagonal members. At one moment these might be under compression, at the next under tension. In the early forms of cast-iron bridges these changes weakened the structure and often caused its failure.

STEEL 1

In relation to its weight steel is the strongest of all bridge-building materials. It is twenty per cent stronger than wrought iron. More important still is the fact that steel is the only economical structural material whose tensile strength is equal to, or exceeds, its compressive strength.

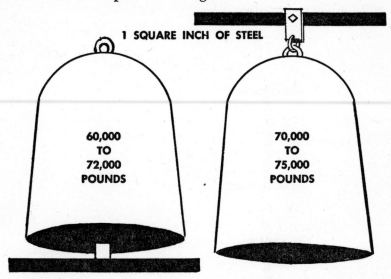

1 SQUARE INCH OF STEEL

60,000 TO 72,000 POUNDS

70,000 TO 75,000 POUNDS

The flexibility of steel makes it an ideal material for the construction of the towers on suspension bridges. The pull of the cables often moves the top of these towers two or three feet from true perpendicular.

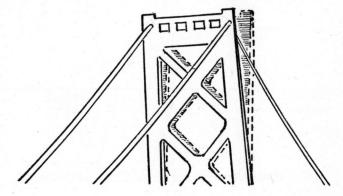

STEEL 2

COMMON SHAPES OF STRUCTURAL STEEL
MEMBERS

Through the use of these prefabricated, standard shapes, steel-bridge construction is now swift and economical. Today each structural member is fabricated with great accuracy and can be made to fit within a fraction of an inch.

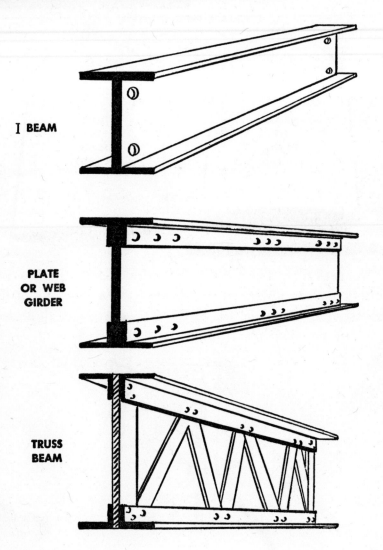

I BEAM

PLATE
OR WEB
GIRDER

TRUSS
BEAM

STEEL 4

In comparing the design of bridges, one senses that the steel arch "leaps" and the suspension bridge "soars," while the arms

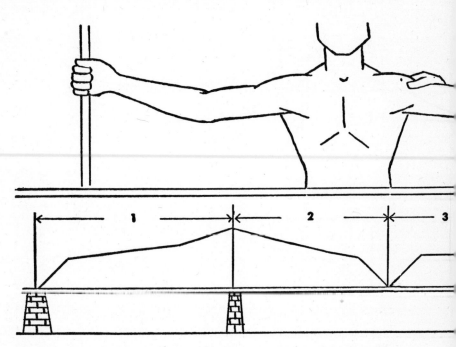

The structural design of the cantilever bridge is based on the balance and counterbalance of the five sections. Sections 1 and 5 are the anchor arms and are attached to the two abutments. These anchor arms counterbalance sections 2 and 4, the cantilever arms, as well as section 3, the suspended span.

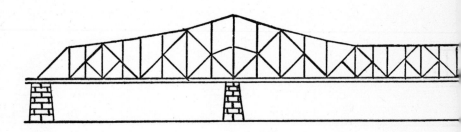

STEEL 4

of the cantilever seem to "reach out" in order to span the space that has to be bridged.

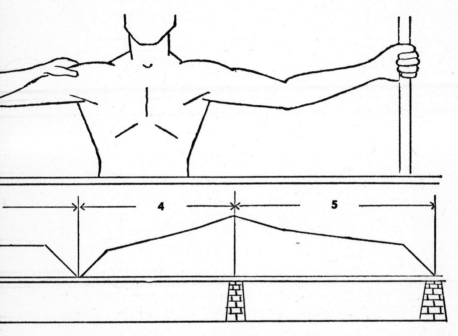

The extreme span length of cantilever bridges is about the same as that of steel arches, but their carrying capacity is not as great. In this kind of structure the stress of moving loads sets up a highly complex system of strains. At one moment a steel member may be under tension, and at the next, as the load passes, it may be under compression.

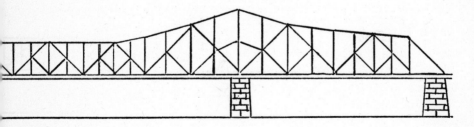

STEEL 5

A suspension bridge would sag like a clothesline unless there
were some way of distributing the load along the length of the

Aside from the towers, all main structural members of a suspension bridge are in constant tension. Each tower bears half
the total weight of the bridge. Through the use of special high-
tension steel cables the span lengths of suspension bridges have

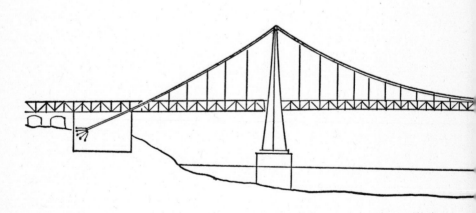

STEEL 5

bridge. A stiffening truss placed below the deck of the bridge not only distributes the load more evenly, but helps to stabilize the bridge in high winds.

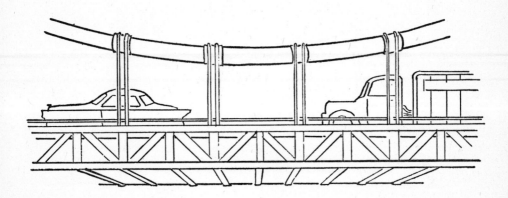

been increased to 4200 feet, or nearly three-quarters of a mile. The maximum carrying capacity of long-span suspension bridges, though entirely adequate for the vehicular traffic that they bear, is only one-third to one-eighth as great as that of the steel arch or the cantilever bridge.

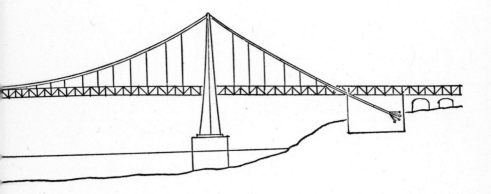

CEMENT CONCRETE 1 (REINFORCED)

Cement concrete is a man-made, synthetic stone. The fact that concrete can be be molded or cast in a great variety of shapes makes it an invaluable bridgebuilding material. Its ultimate strength under compression is less than that of granite, and, like natural stone, it has little tensile strength.

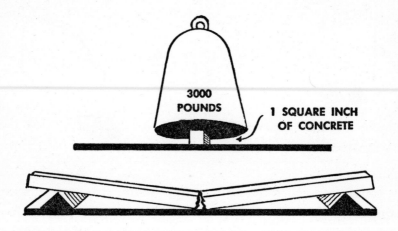

When steel rods are embedded in concrete its ultimate strength both in compression and tension is greatly reinforced. The tensile strength of reinforced concrete is equal to or greater than its compressive strength.

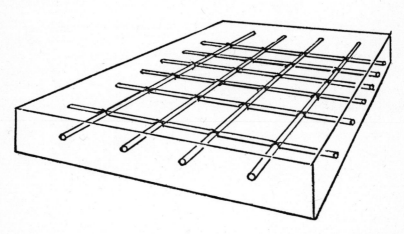

CEMENT CONCRETE 2 (REINFORCED)

In a reinforced-concrete beam the steel rods are placed in that part of the beam which is under tension.

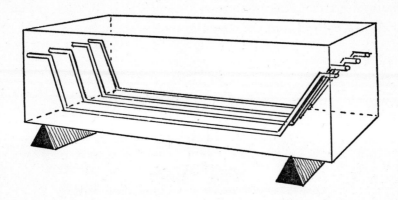

Reinforced-concrete bridges are more extensively used abroad than in this country. Our bridge engineers have developed a short-span reinforced-concrete bridge that is known as a rigid-frame bridge. This type of bridge is usually built for vehicular traffic and has become the standard over- or underpass bridge used on our modern expressways.

CEMENT CONCRETE 4 (PRESTRESSED)

Through a method of prestressing, the tensile strength of concrete can be reinforced without using steel rods.

The dead weight of an unsupported concrete beam, like that of natural stone, over a long span will cause it to crack.

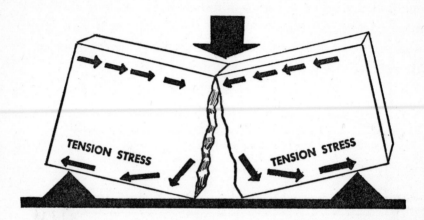

If a concrete beam is subjected to a sufficiently high compressive force at the points indicated by the arrows, the compressive stress thus produced will offset the usual tension stress that the beam develops in supporting its own weight.

Compressive stress runs throughout the length of the beam.

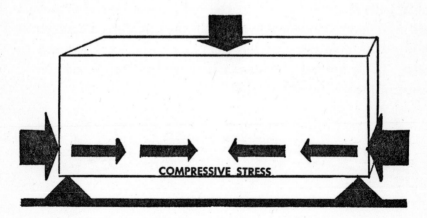

CEMENT CONCRETE 3 (PRESTRESSED)

The prestress is created by imbedding a series of parallel, high-grade steel wires through the full length of the beam. By means of screws or jacks these wires are tightened until a powerful compressive stress has been established in the full length of the beam. It has been found that a working stress of about 65 tons per square inch on these wires will make the beam not only self-supporting but capable of carrying an additional load equal to half its own dead weight.

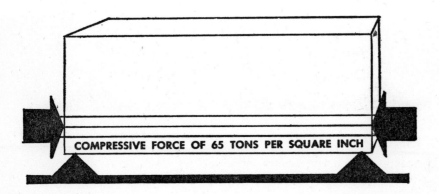

COMPRESSIVE FORCE OF 65 TONS PER SQUARE INCH

In the last few years, prestressed-concrete bridges have been built with span lengths up to 500 feet. These new structures are even more economical in materials than reinforced-concrete bridges using 50 per cent less steel and 25 per cent less concrete. These bridges also have a very modern appearance because of their slender grace.

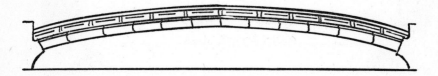

INDEX

Index